iQ Puzzle Book Challenge

k

Kandour Ltd

Kandour Ltd
1-3 Colebrooke Place, London N1 8HZ
UNITED KINGDOM

First published 2006

10 9 8 7 6 5 4 3 2 1

Kandour Ltd has made every effort to ensure that the content of this book was accurate at the
time of publication. The publisher, author, and editors cannot be held liable for any errors and
omissions in this publication or actions that may be taken as a consequence of using it.

Managing Editor: James Jackson
Production: Carol Titchener
Author: G. Newton
Jacket Design: Alexander Rose Publishing Limited
Puzzle Layout: Domex e-Data Pvt Ltd

Printed and bound in China

ISBN-13: 978-1-905741-28-1

CONTENTS

We have split each section into:

- E for Easy

- M for Medium

- D for Difficult

Once you find the difficult puzzles easy you will know you are an IQ Master!

Numerical

- **Find the missing number.**

1.

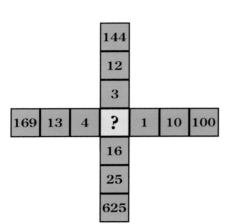

144	
12	
3	

169	13	4	?	1	10	100

16	
25	
625	

9	5	10	8
A	B	C	D

2.

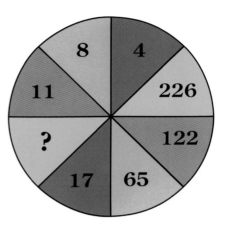

50	5	35	15
A	B	C	D

3.

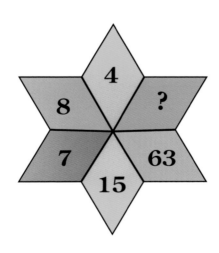

47	50	48	49
A	B	C	D

4.

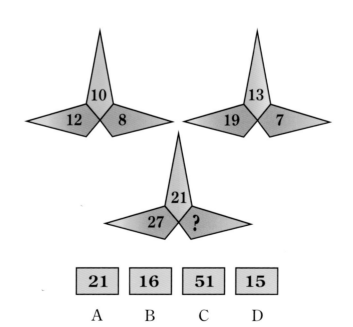

21	16	51	15
A	B	C	D

5.

4	8	9	6
A	B	C	D

6.

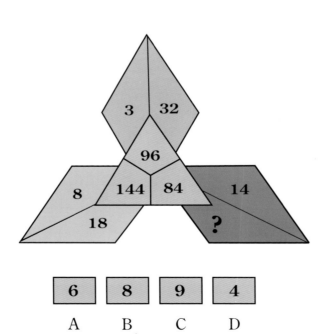

6	8	9	4
A	B	C	D

M

7.

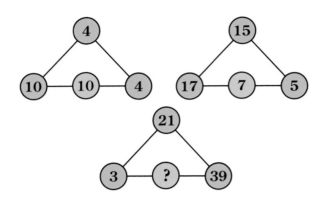

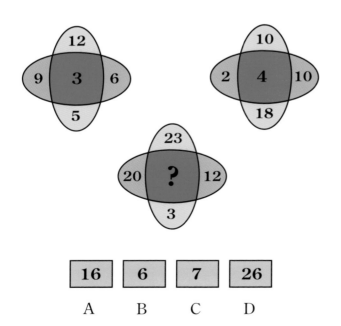

12	21	31	29
A	B	C	D

8.

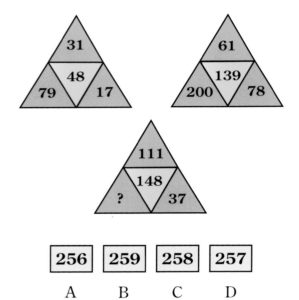

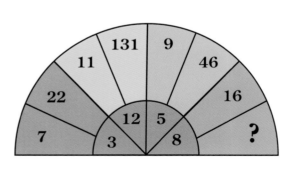

256	259	258	257
A	B	C	D

9.

16	6	7	26
A	B	C	D

10.

130	129	127	128
A	B	C	D

8

11.

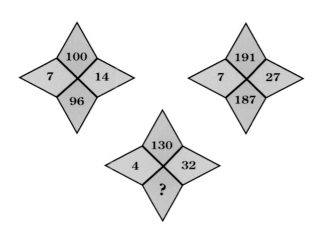

36	28	128	126
A	B	C	D

12.

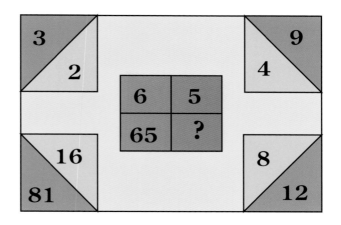

44	65	14	96
A	B	C	D

13.

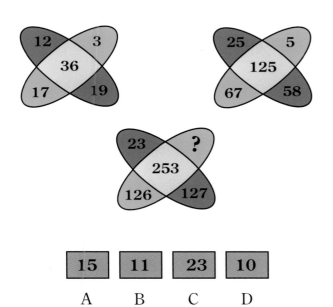

15	11	23	10
A	B	C	D

14.

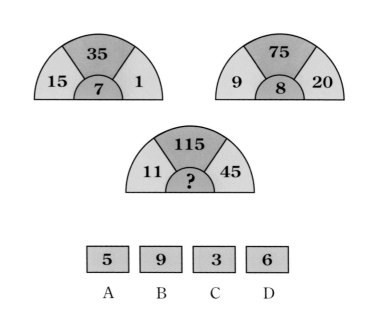

5	9	3	6
A	B	C	D

15.

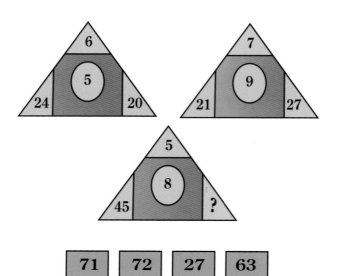

71	72	27	63
A	B	C	D

16.

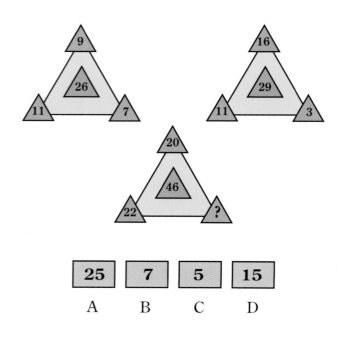

25	7	5	15
A	B	C	D

17.

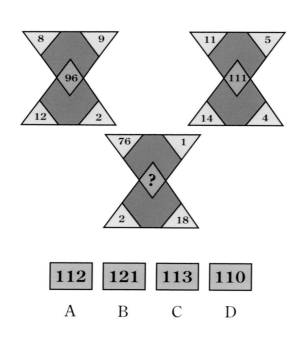

112	121	113	110
A	B	C	D

18.

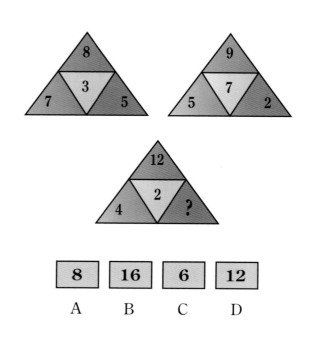

8	16	6	12
A	B	C	D

19.

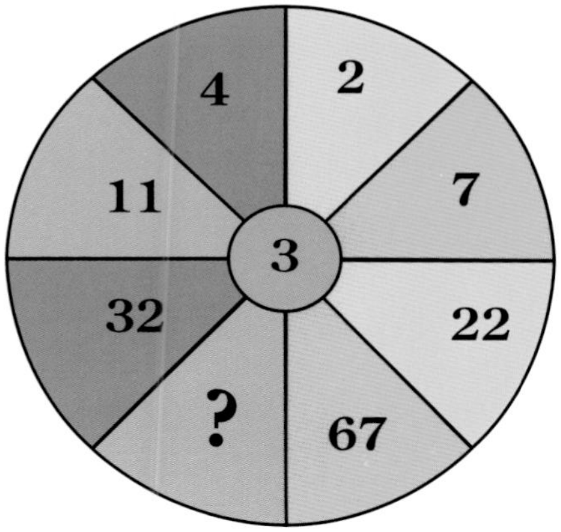

96	95	97	200
A	B	C	D

20.

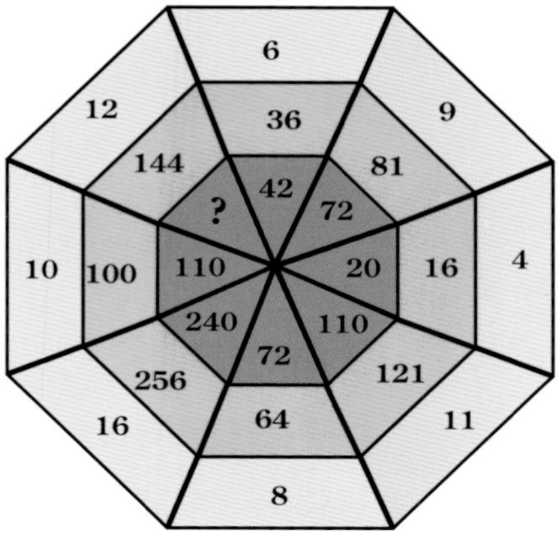

132	133	156	32
A	B	C	D

21.

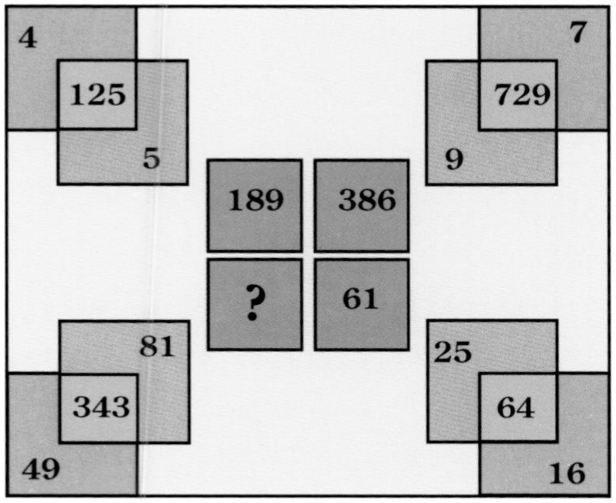

1072	386	1074	1070
A	B	C	D

22.

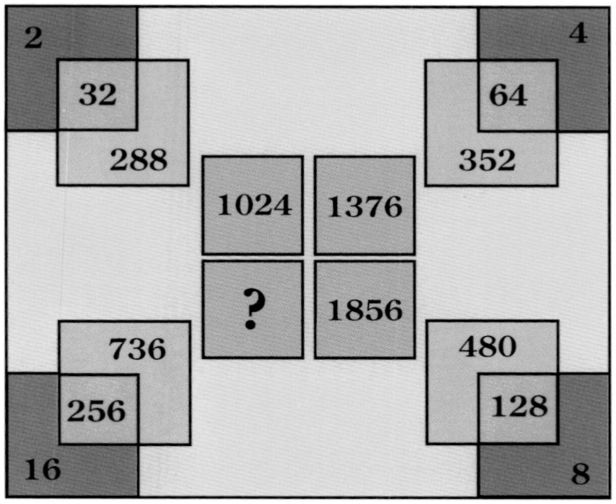

1120	2592	2593	1121
A	B	C	D

23.

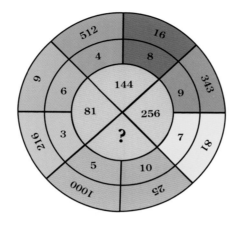

224	225	252	256
A	B	C	D

24.

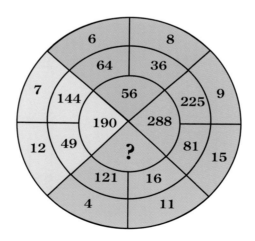

211	220	137	210
A	B	C	D

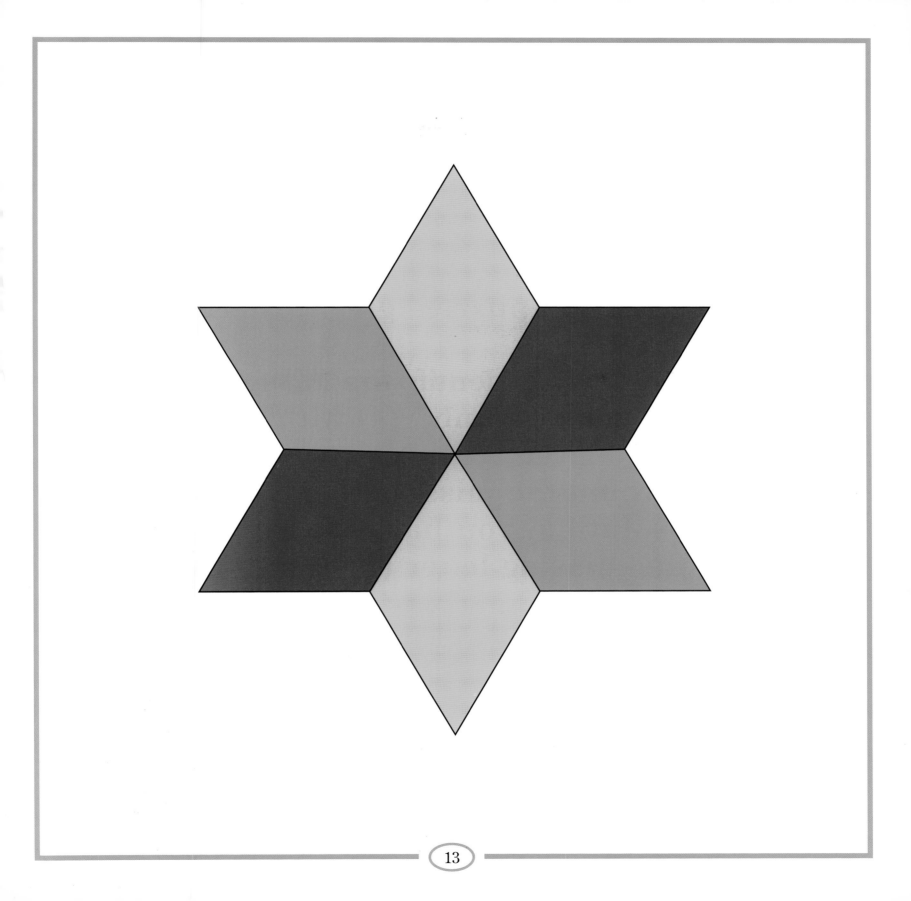

OBSERVATION

- In each of the puzzles given, there is a missing letter.
- You have to first identify the missing letter.
- There is also a number(s) with a plus or minus sign given.
- Do not count the missing letter. To arrive at the solution, you have to count ahead from the missing letter (in case of '+') or backwards from the missing letter (in case of '-').
- Try solving puzzles in the easy and medium category in two minutes, and puzzles in the difficult category in one minute.

1.

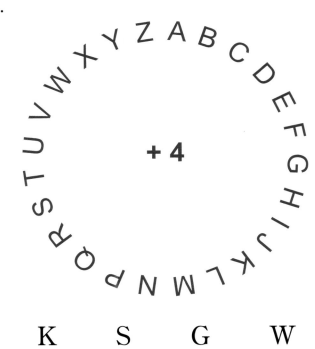

K S G W

2.

A H F Y

3.

-2

L K R O

4.

Q T Y P

5.

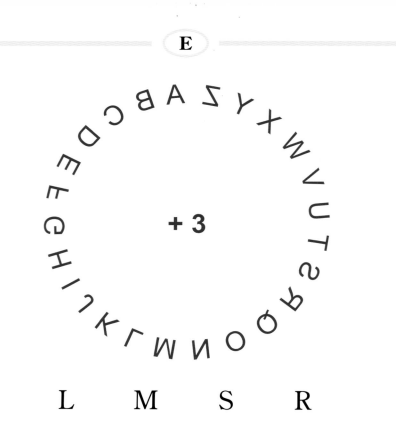

L   M   S   R

6.

+ 15

T   R   A   S

7.

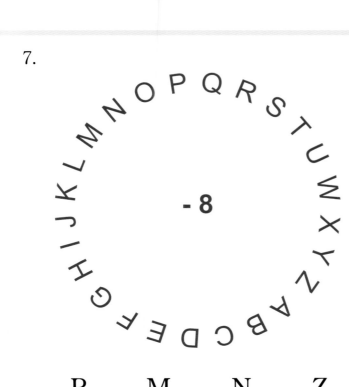

- 8

P   M   N   Z

8.

- 18

U   F   V   E

9.

+ 23

P   E   Y   G

10.

- 10

M   T   K   S

11.

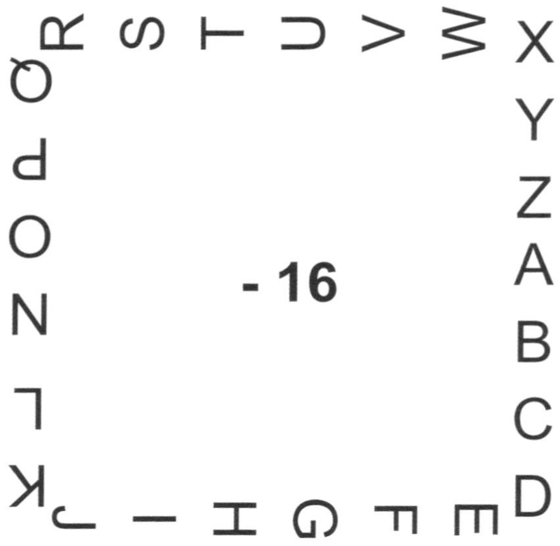

- 16

C   W   R   F

12.

+ 4

E   P   B   M

13.

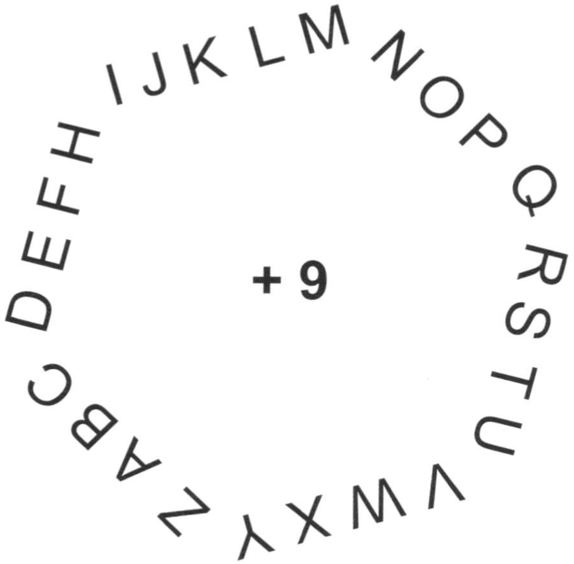

+ 9

Q   R   P   O

14.

- 12

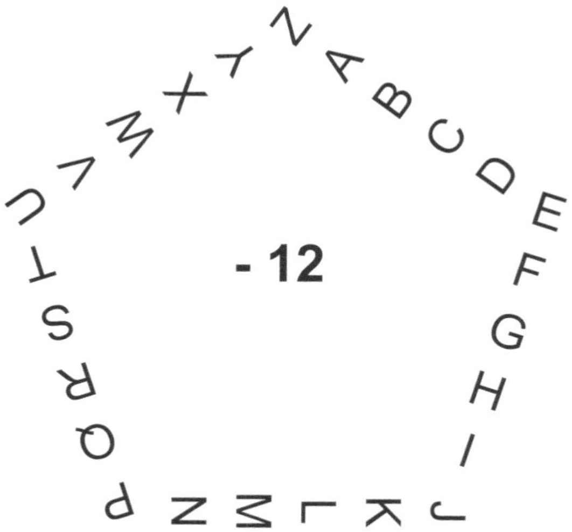

Z   A   D   C

15.

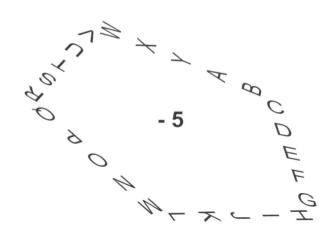

- 5

U   D   E   W

16.

+ 7

N   O   Y   P

17.

- 11

O   K   F   G

18.

+ 8
- 3

K   H   F   G

19.

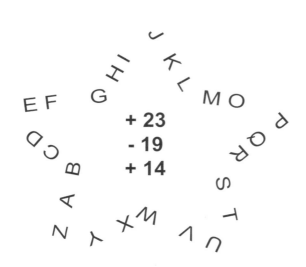

+ 23
- 19
+ 14

S   H   F   T

20.

+ 9   - 15   + 6

r   Q   S   p

21.

- 13   + 25   - 9

L   K   P   k

22.

+ 1   - 16   + 5

s   T   u   q

23.

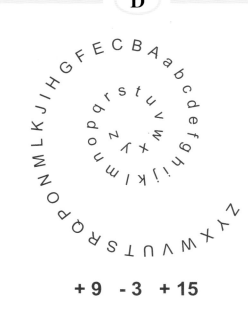

+ 9   - 3   + 15

M   h   r   o

24.

+ 19   - 40   + 9

J   E   m   G

ANALOGIES

- **The first figure is related to the second one. Similarly, which figure is related to the third figure?**

1.

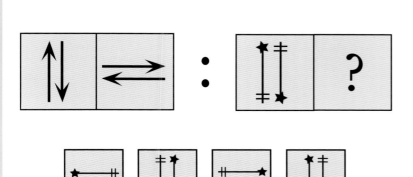

A   B   C   D

2.

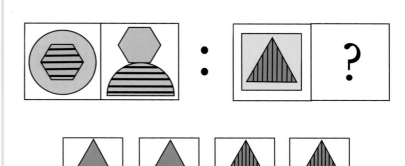

A   B   C   D

3.

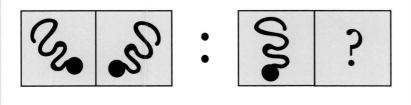

A   B   C   D

4.

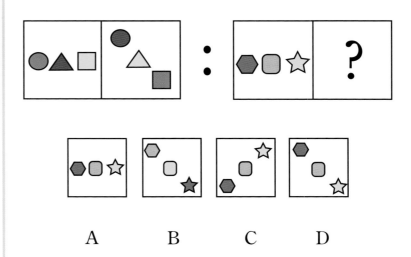

A   B   C   D

5.

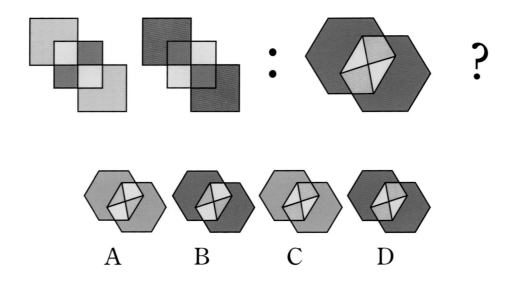

A   B   C   D

6.

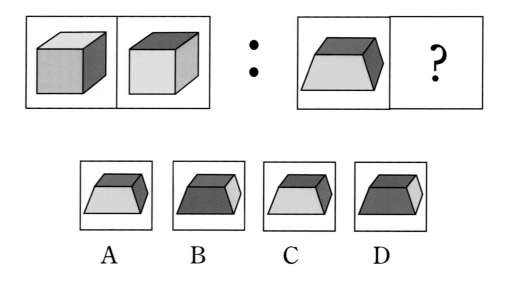

A   B   C   D

7.

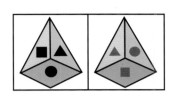   :

A   B   C   D

8.

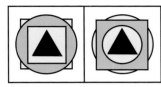   :

A   B   C   D

9.

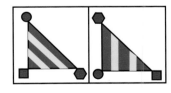 :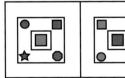

A   B   C   D

10.

 :

A   B   C   D

11.

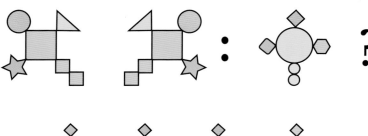

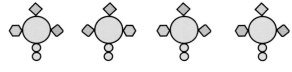

A	B	C	D

12.

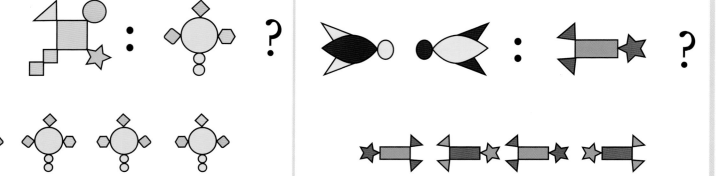

A	B	C	D

13.

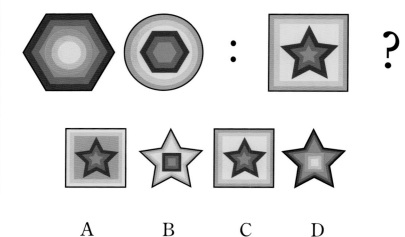

A	B	C	D

14.

A	B	C	D

15.

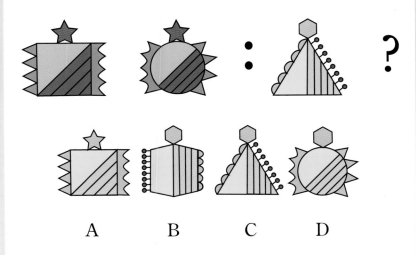

A   B   C   D

16.

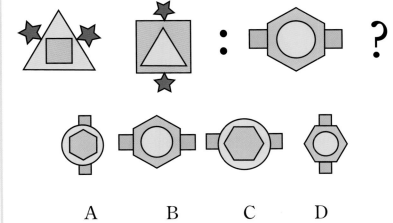

A   B   C   D

17.

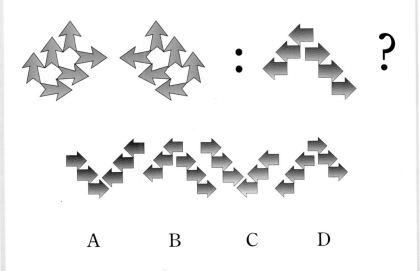

A   B   C   D

18.

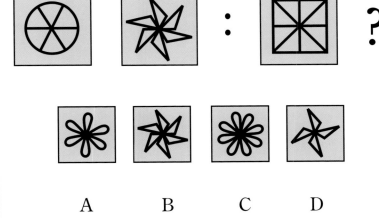

A   B   C   D

19.

A   B   C   D

20.

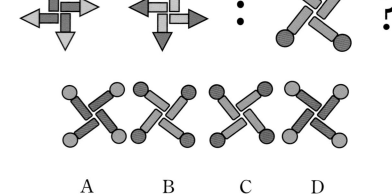

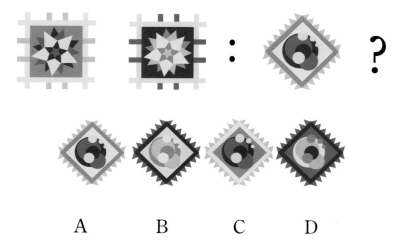

A   B   C   D

21.

A   B   C   D

22.

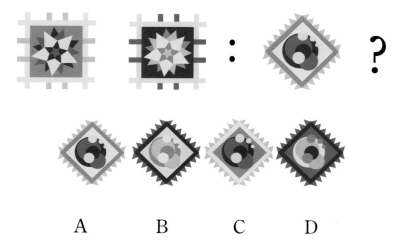

A   B   C   D

23.

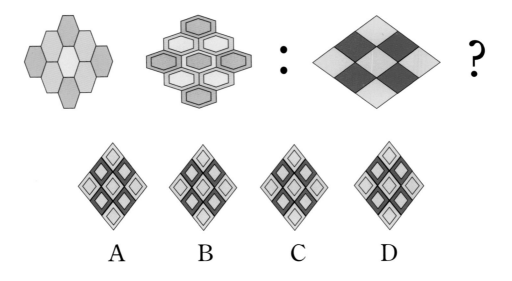

A   B   C   D

24.

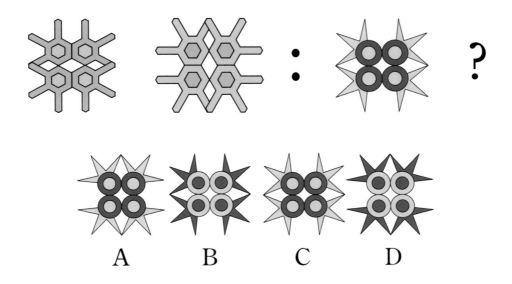

A   B   C   D

CATEGORY

- In each of the given puzzles, only one out of all the figures is different.
- Which is the odd one out?

1.

  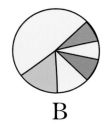

A   B   C

D   E

2.

 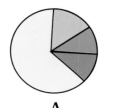 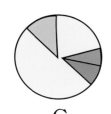

A   B   C

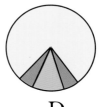 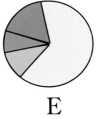

D   E

3.

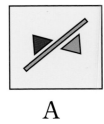 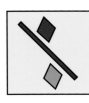

A   B   C

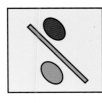

D   E

4.

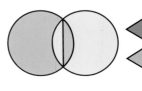 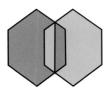

A   B   C

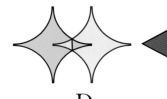 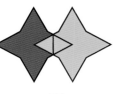

D   E

5.

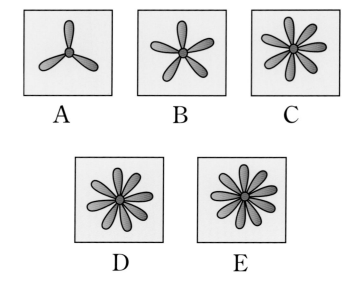

6.

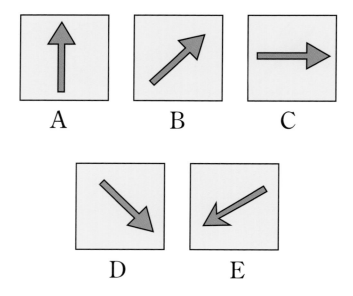

7.

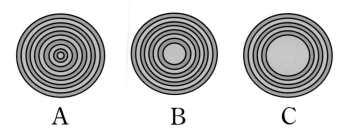

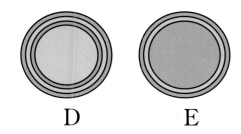

A B C

D E

8.

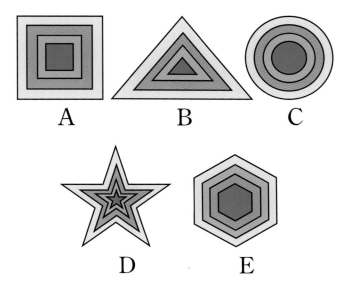

A B C

D E

9.

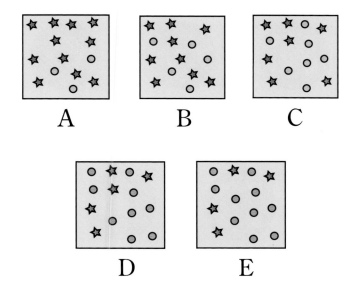

A B C

D E

10.

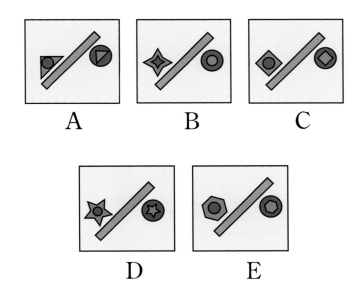

A B C

D E

11.

A   B   C

 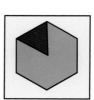

D   E

12.

 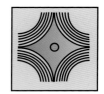 

A   B   C

D   E

13.

 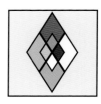 

A   B   C

D   E

14.

A   B   C

D   E

16.

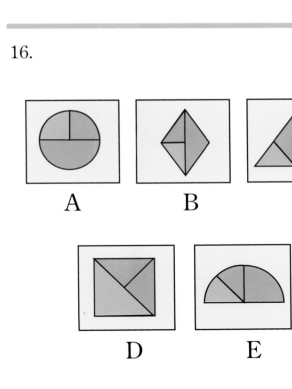

17.

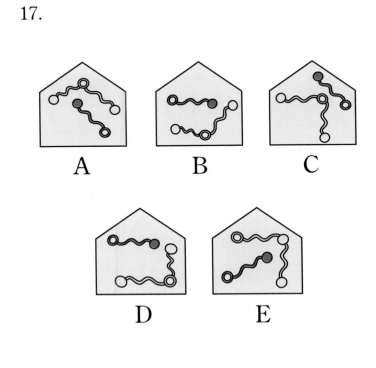

18.

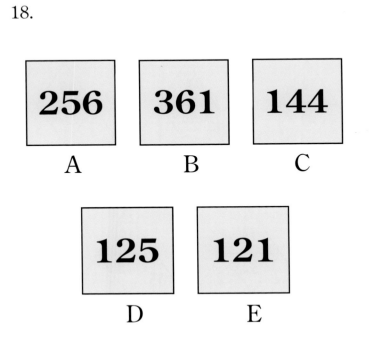

19.

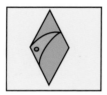 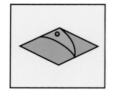 

A   B   C

D   E

20.

A   B   C

D   E

21.

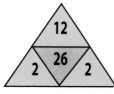 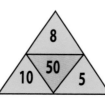

A   B   C

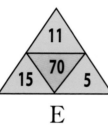 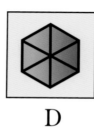

D   E

22.

 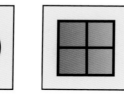

A   B   C

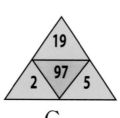 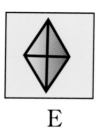

D   E

23.

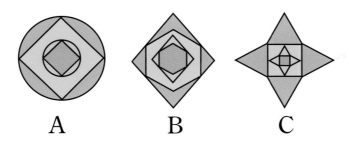

A   B   C

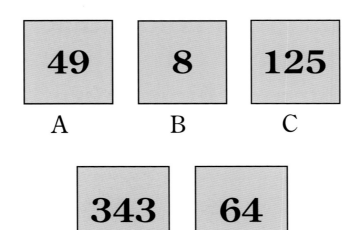

D   E

24.

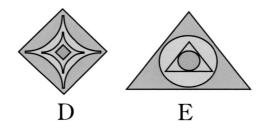

49	8	125
A	B	C

343	64
D	E

MATCH

- In each of the given puzzles, one of the options given is identical to the problem figure.
- Identify the matching figure.

1.

A   B

C   D

2.

A   B

C   D

3.

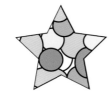

A   B

C   D

4.

A   B

C   D

5.

A

B

C

D

6.

A

B

C

D

7.

A   B

 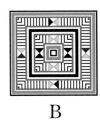

C   D

8.

A   B

A   B

C   D

9.

A   B

C   D

10.

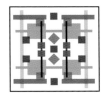

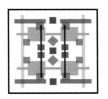 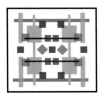

A   B

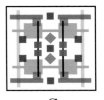 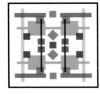

C   D

11.

A

B

C

D

12.

A

B

C

D

13.

A

B

C

D

14.

A

B

C

D

15.

A    B

C    D

16.

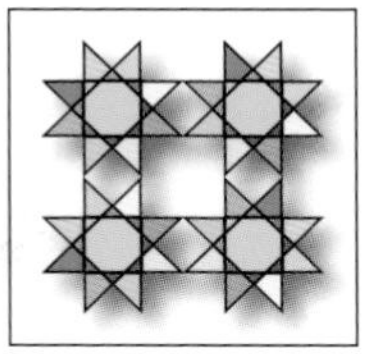

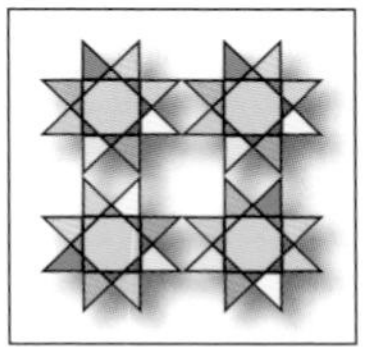

A 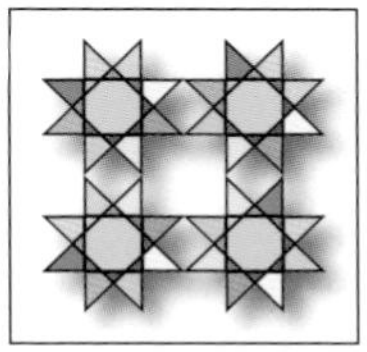   B

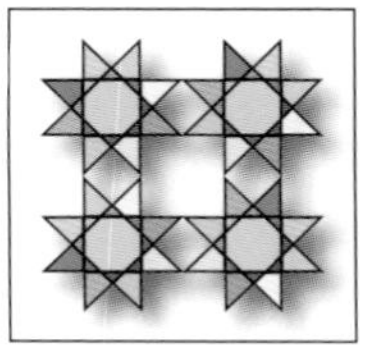

C 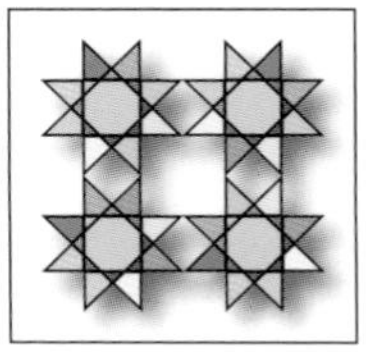   D

17.

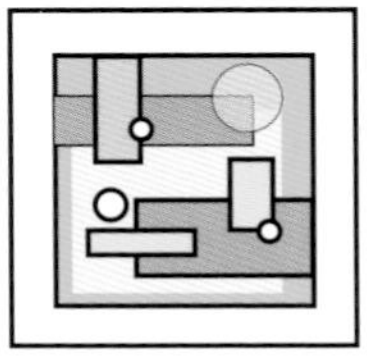

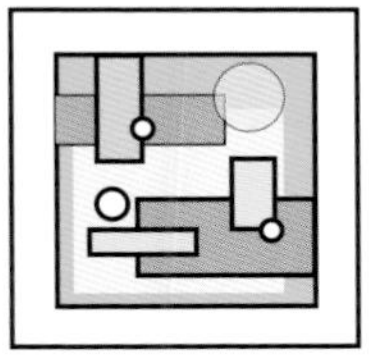

A 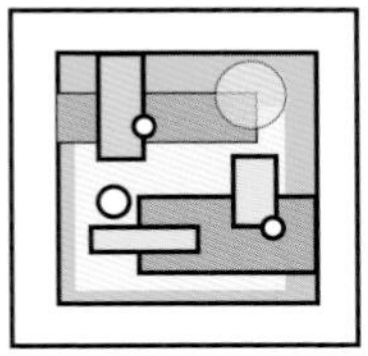   B

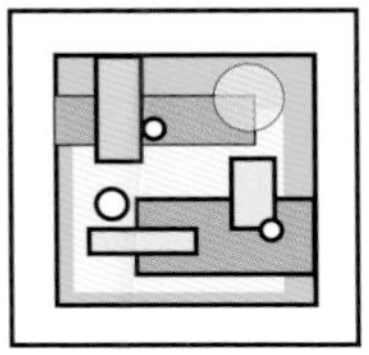

C 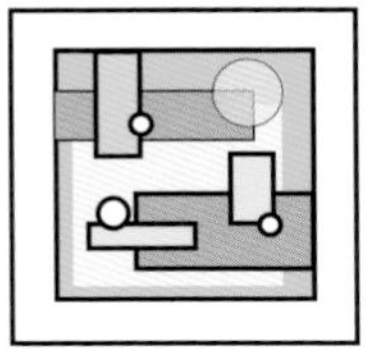   D

18.

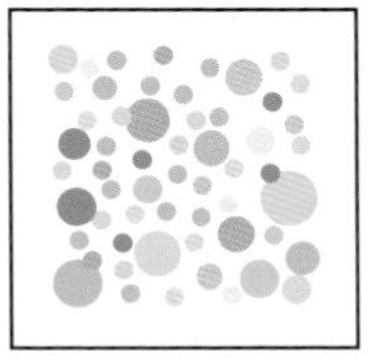

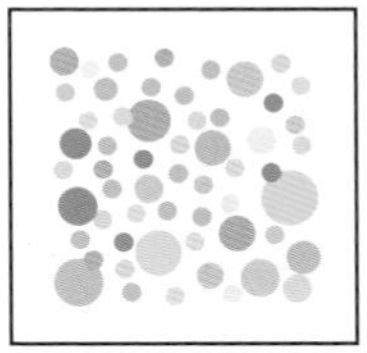

A 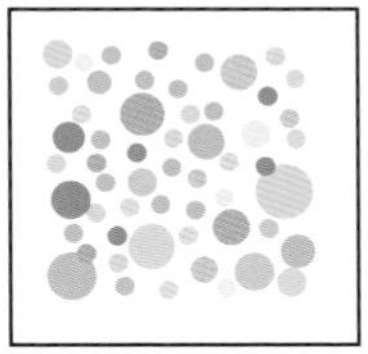   B

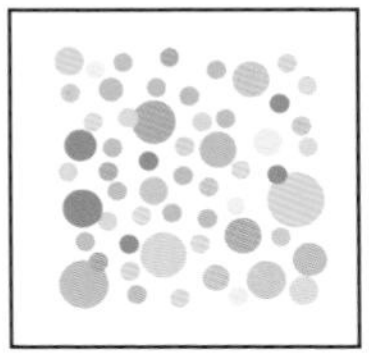

C 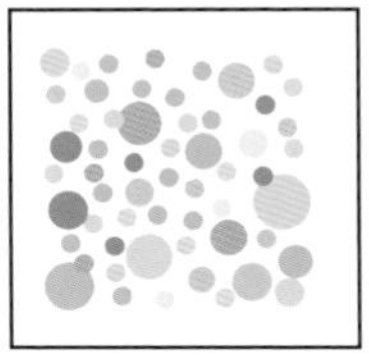   D

19.

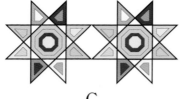

A

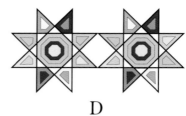

B

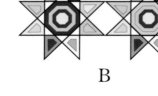

C

D

20.

A

B

C

D

21.

A   B

 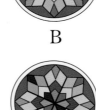

C   D

22.

A   B

 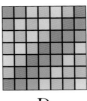

C   D

23.

A   B

C   D

24.

A   B

C   D

25.

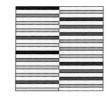

A

B

C

D

26.

A

B

C

D

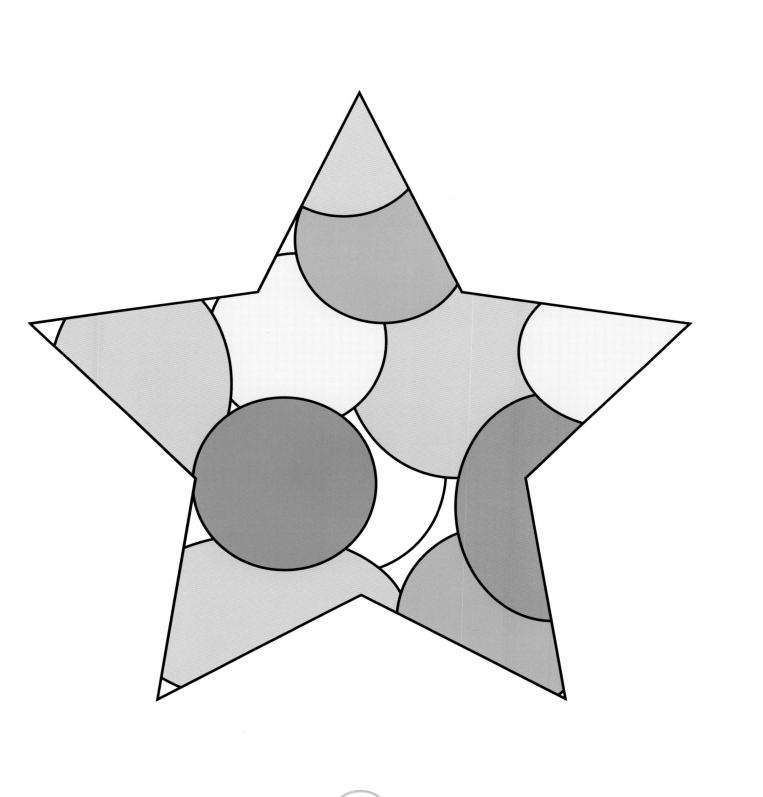

WATER REFLECTION

- **In each of the puzzles which of the options is the water reflection of the problem image?**

1.

A

B

C

D

2.

A

B

C

D

3.

A

B

C

D

4.

A

B

C

D

5.

A

B

C

D

6.

A

B

C

D

7.

A

B

C

D

8.

A

B

C

D

9.

A

B

C

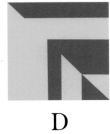

D

10.

A

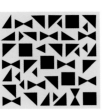

B

C

D

11.

A

B

C

D

12.

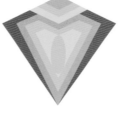

A

B

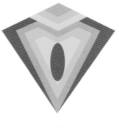

C

D

13.

A

B

C

D

14.

A

B

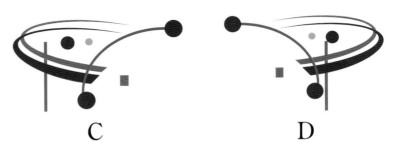

C

D

15.

A

B

C

D

16.

A

B

C

D

17.

A

B

C

D

18.

A

B

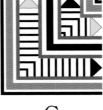

C

D

19.

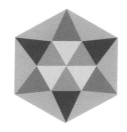

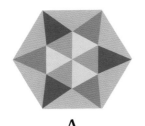

A

B

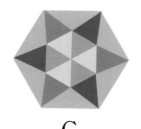

C

D

20.

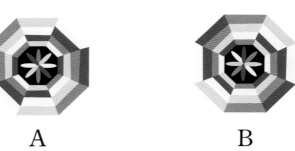

A

B

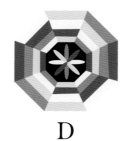

C

D

21.

A

B

C

D

22.

A

B

C

D

23.

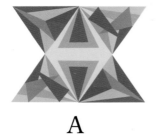

A

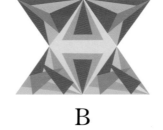

B

C

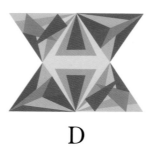

D

24.

A

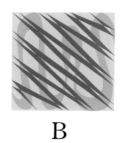

B

C

D

SEQUENCE

- The presented problem figures follow a certain sequence.
- Think logically to find the answer that would be the next in the sequence.

1.

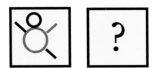

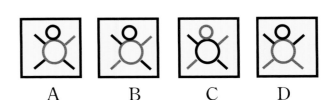

A   B   C   D

2.

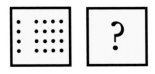

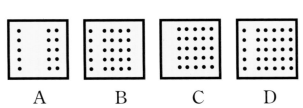

A   B   C   D

3.

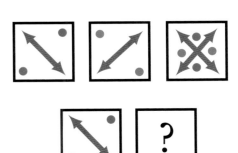

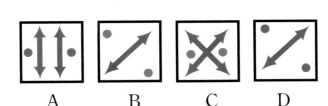

A   B   C   D

4.

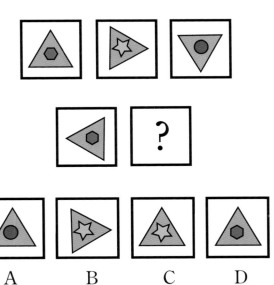

A   B   C   D

5.

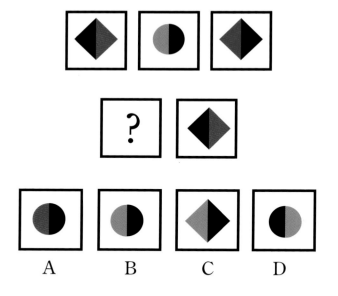

6.

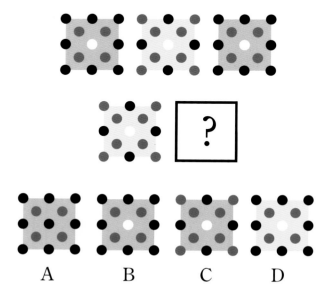

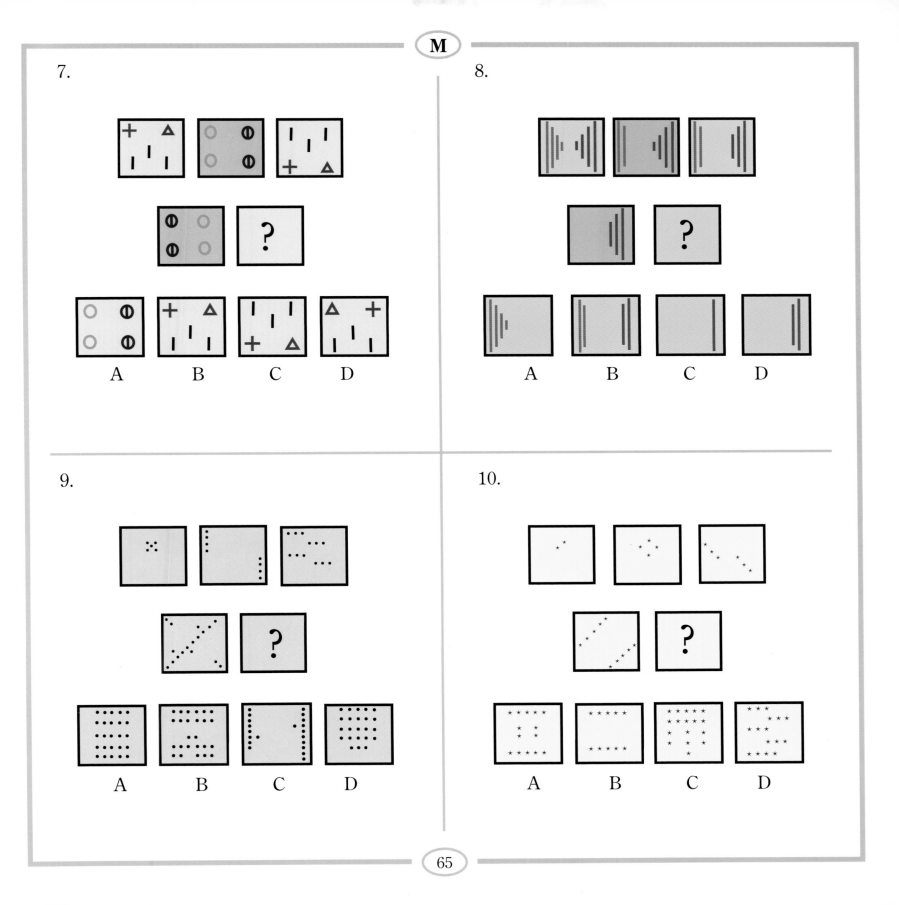

7.

8.

9.

10.

A   B   C   D

11.

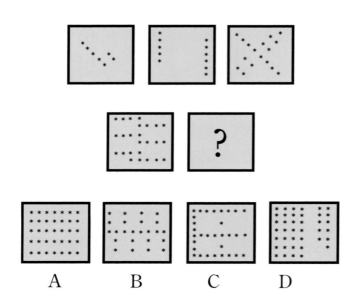

A   B   C   D

12.

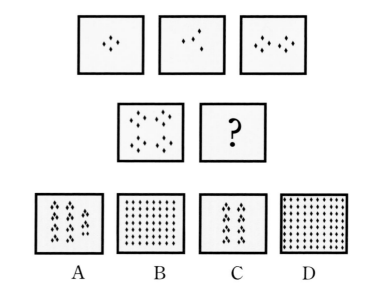

A   B   C   D

13.

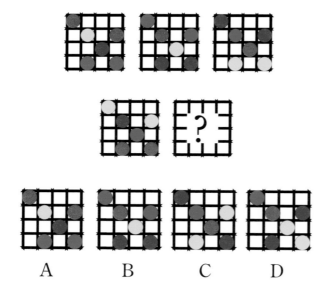

A   B   C   D

14.

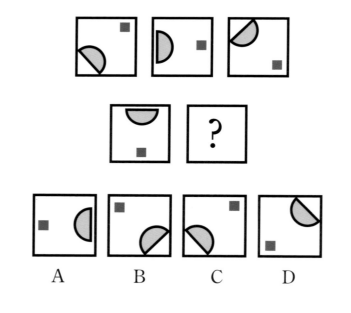

A   B   C   D

15.

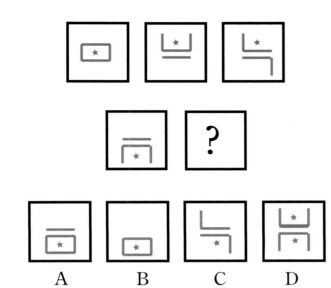

A B C D

16.

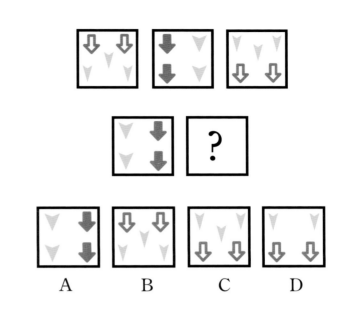

A B C D

17.

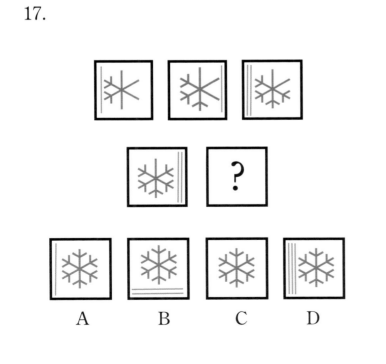

A B C D

18.

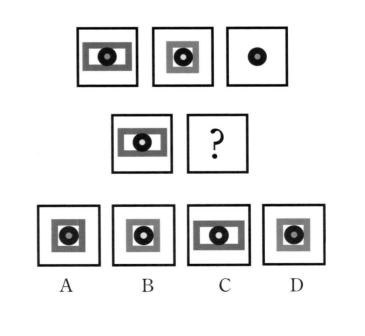

A B C D

19.

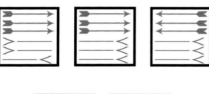
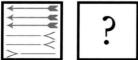
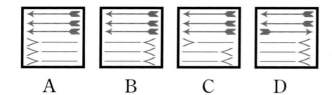
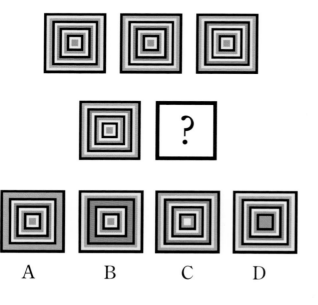

20.

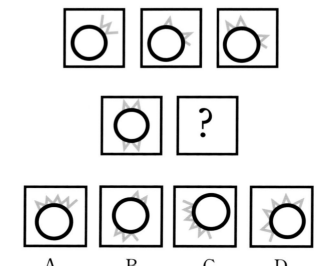
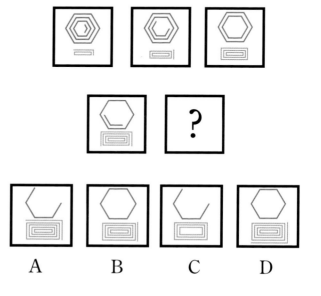

21.

22.

23.

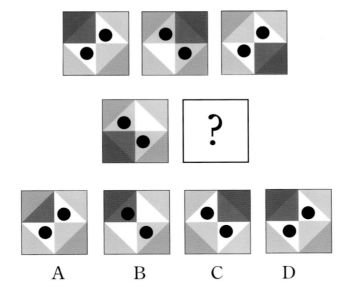

A   B   C   D

24.

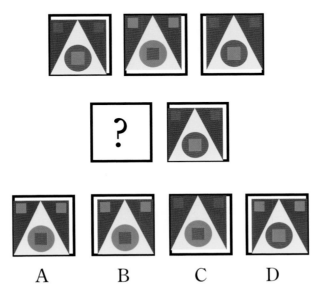

A   B   C   D

SERIES

- **In each of the puzzles given, find the missing figure that will complete the series.**

1.

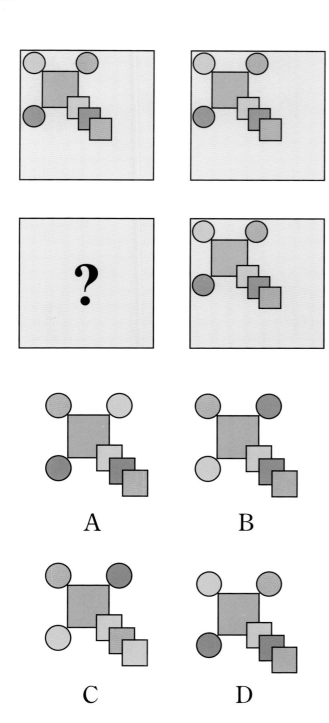

A B

C D

2.

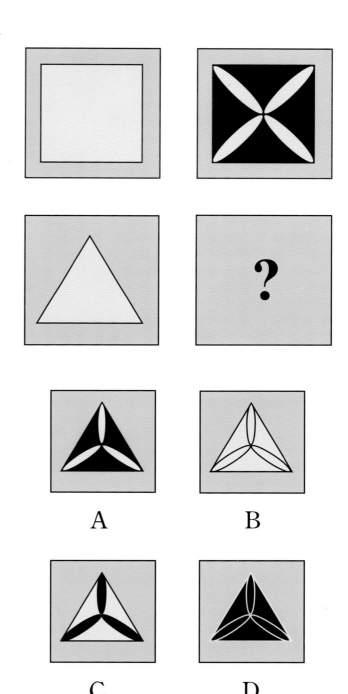

A B

C D

3.

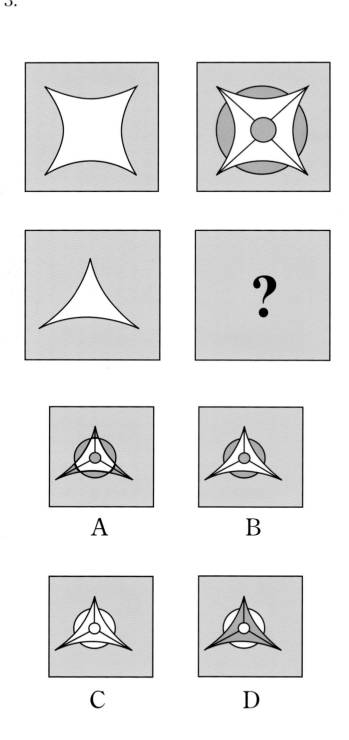

A   B

C   D

4.

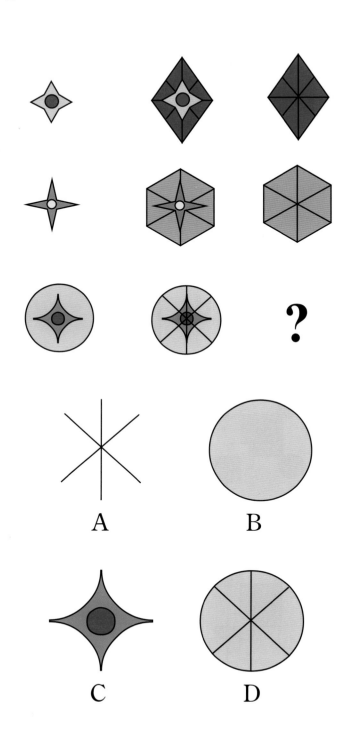

A   B

C   D

5.

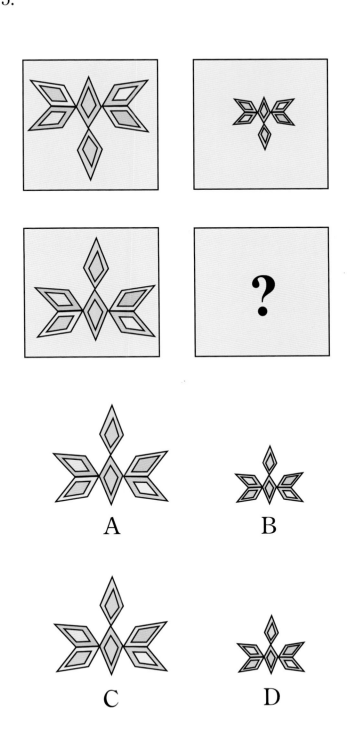

A   B

C   D

6.

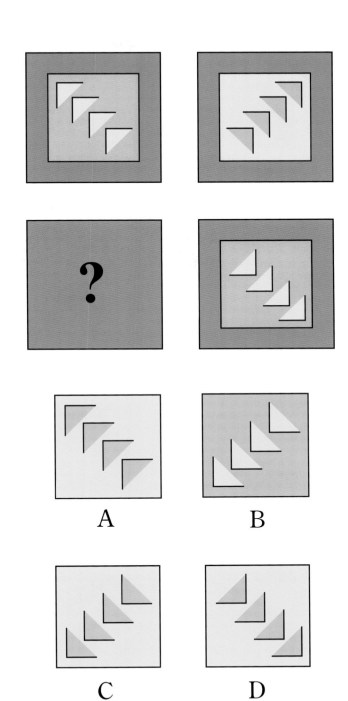

A   B

C   D

7.

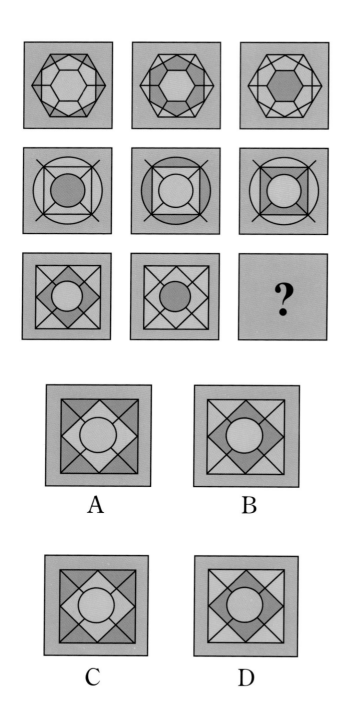

8.

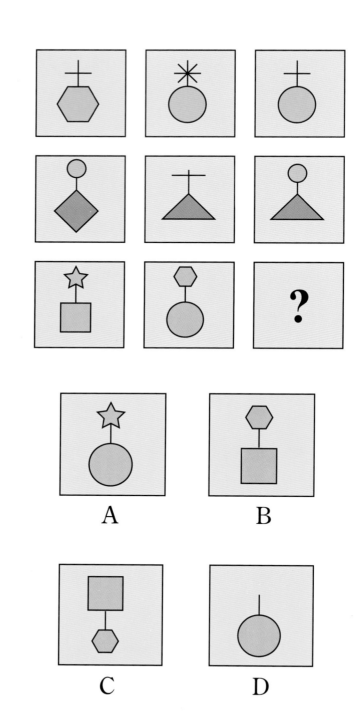

9.

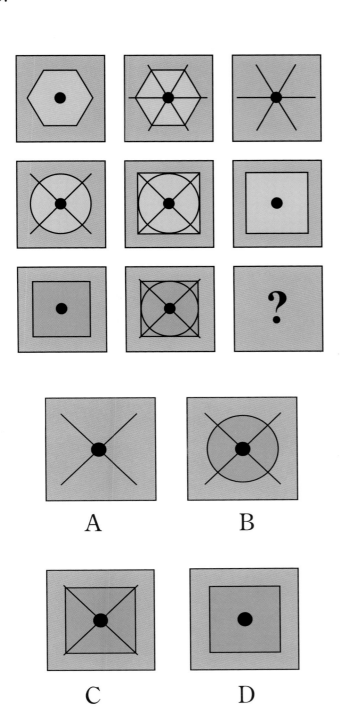

10.

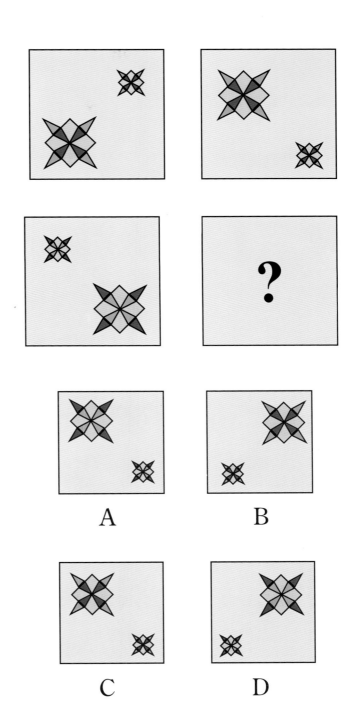

11.

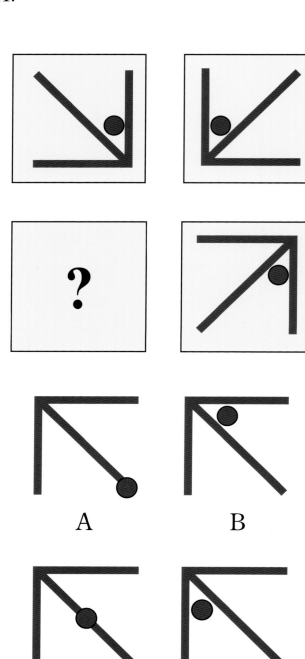

A

B

C

D

12.

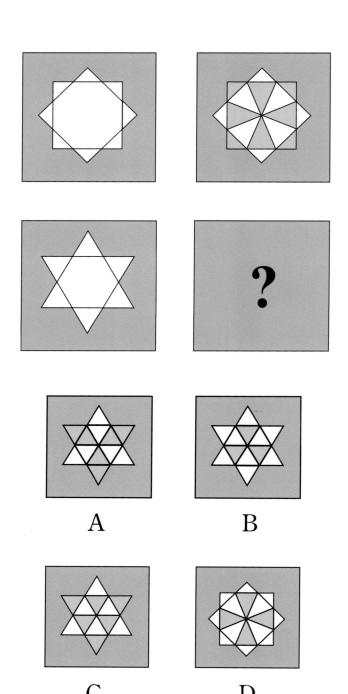

A

B

C

D

13.

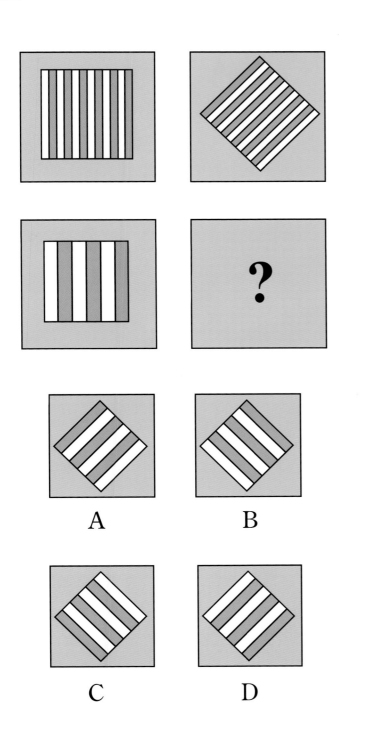

A   B

C   D

14.

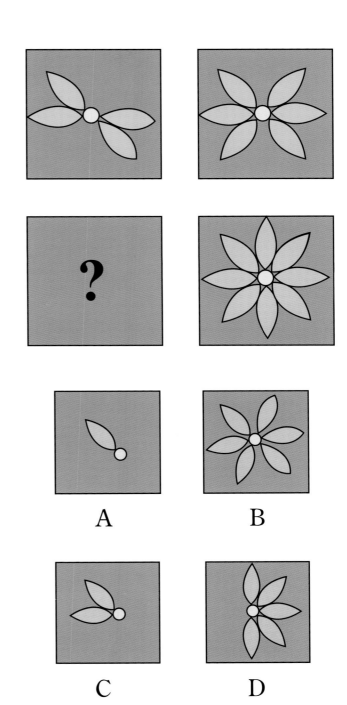

A   B

C   D

15.

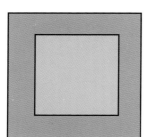 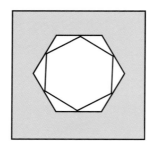

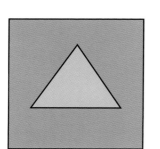 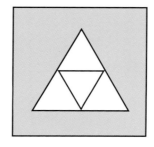

?

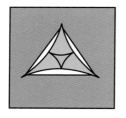 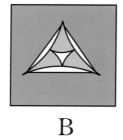

A   B

 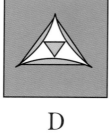

C   D

16.

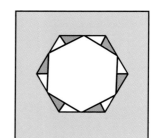 

 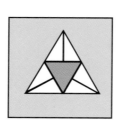

?

 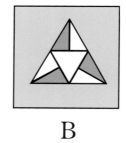

A   B

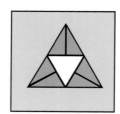

C   D

17.

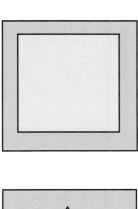 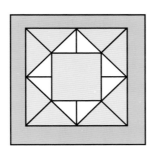

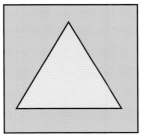

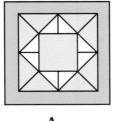 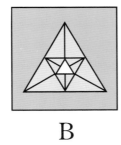

A   B

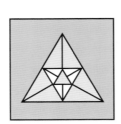

C   D

18.

 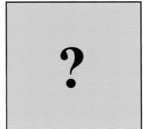

A   B

C   D

79

19.

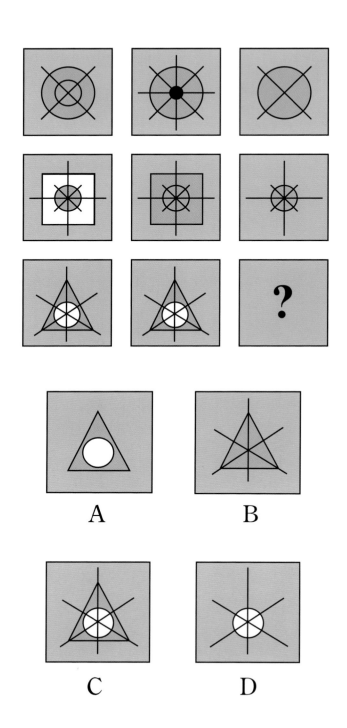

20.

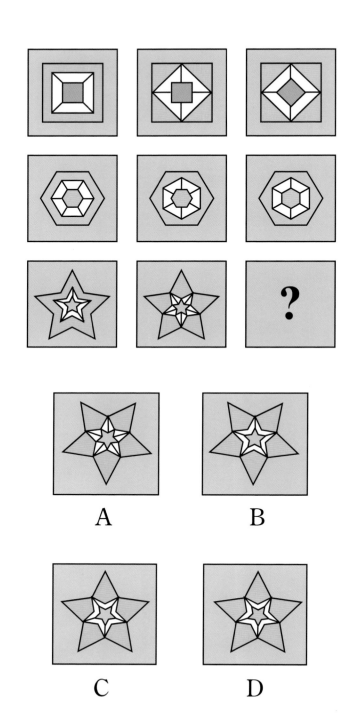

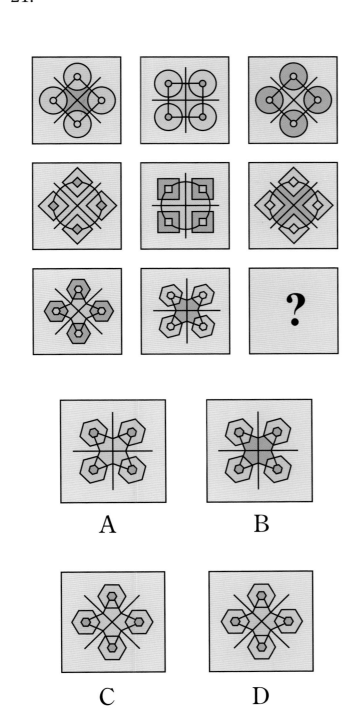

21.

A   B

C   D

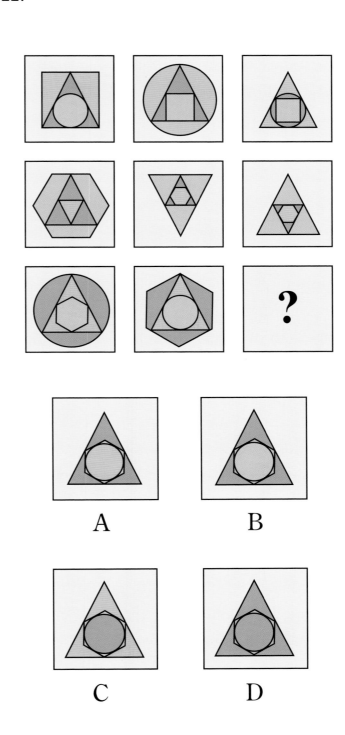

22.

A   B

C   D

23.

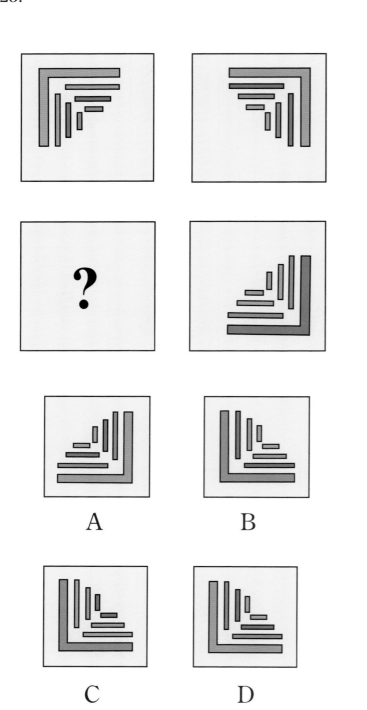

A B

C D

24.

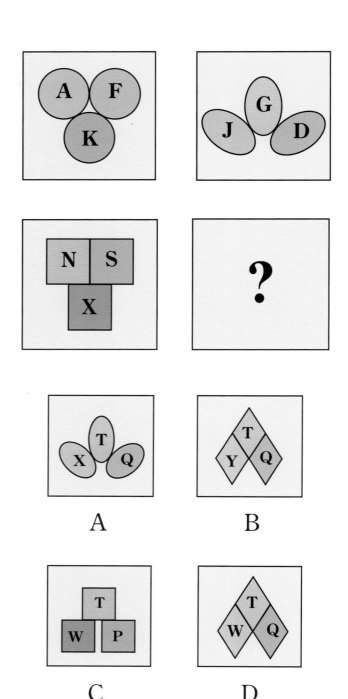

A B

C D

PATTERN

- In the given puzzles, think of the pattern that the cut pieces, if put together, will make.
- There can be only one right answer.

1.

A   B

C   D

2.

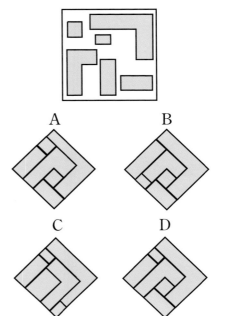

A   B

C   D

3.

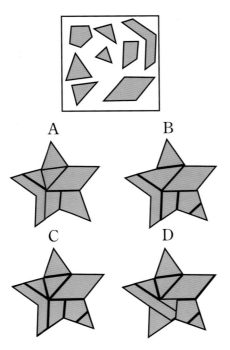

A   B

C   D

4.

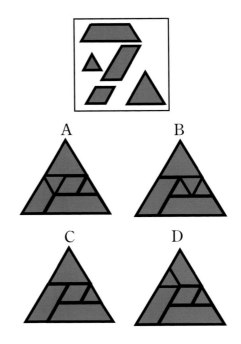

A   B

C   D

5.

A

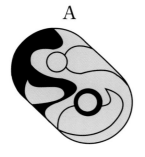

B

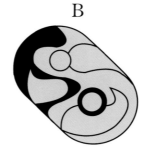

C

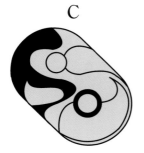

D

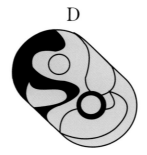

6.

A

B

C

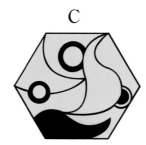

D

7.

A

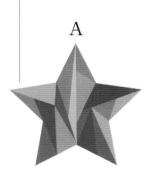

B

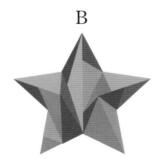

C

D

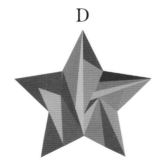

8.

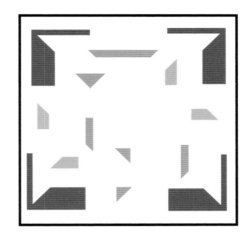

A

B

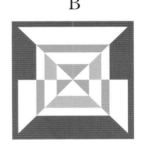

C

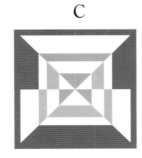

D

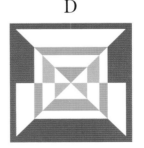

9.

10.

A

B

A

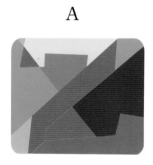

B

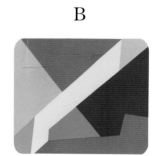

C

D

C

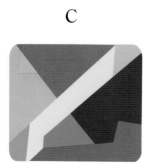

D

11.

A

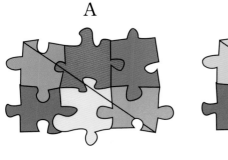

B

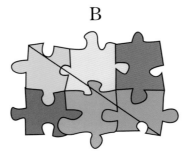

C

12.

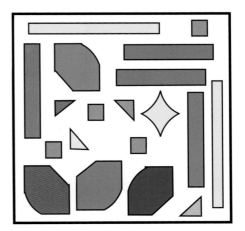

A

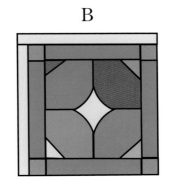

B

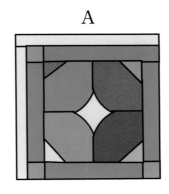

C

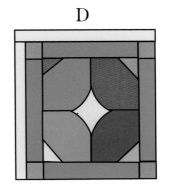

D

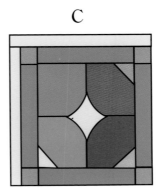

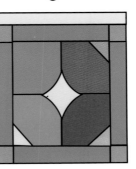

13.

A    B

C    D

14.

A    B

C    D

15.

A

B

C

D

16.

A

B

C

D

17.

18.

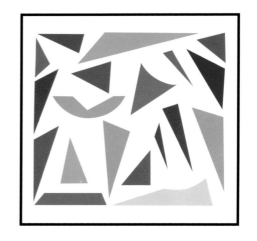

A

B

A

B

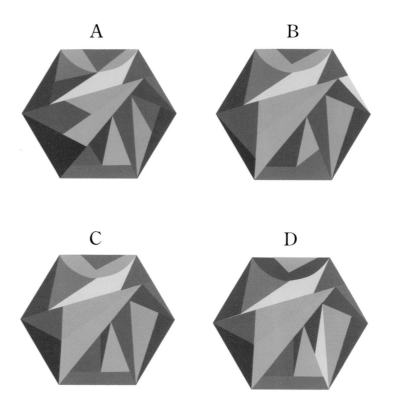

C

D

C

D

19.

A
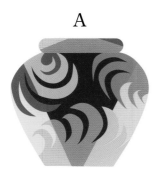

B
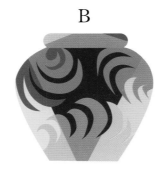

C
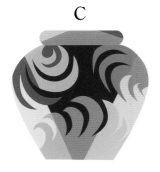

D
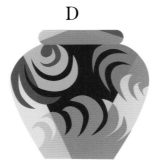

20.

A

B
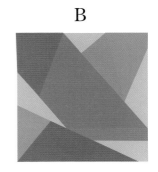

C
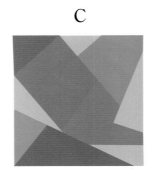

D
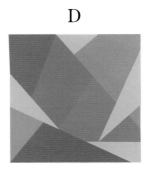

21.

22.

A

B

A

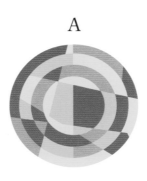

B

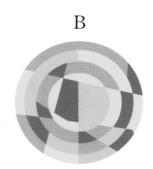

C

D

C

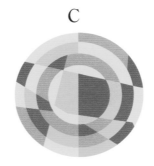

D

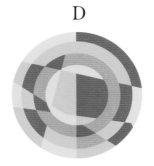

23.

24.

A

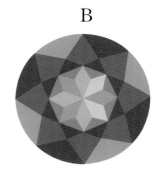

B

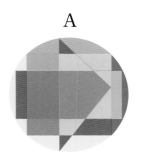

A

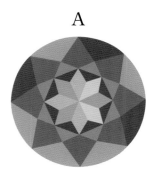

B

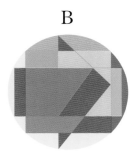

C

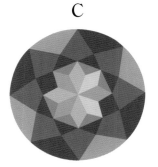

D

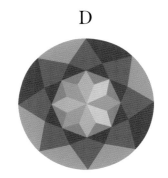

C

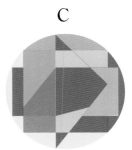

D

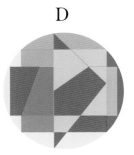

25.

A

B

C

D

26.

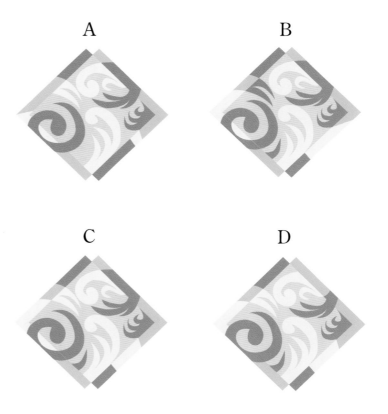

SIMILARITY

- **In the puzzles that follow, you will find two or three rows of figures given.**
- **In the puzzles with two rows, two figures, one from each row, share a similar feature.**
- **In the puzzles with three rows, three figures, one from each row, share a similar feature.**
- **Try and identify the similar figures.**

1.

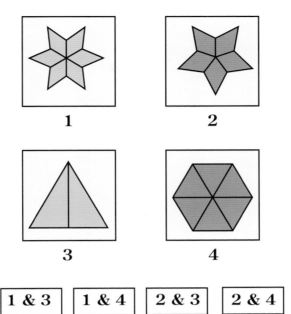

1   2

3   4

1 & 3	1 & 4	2 & 3	2 & 4
A	B	C	D

2.

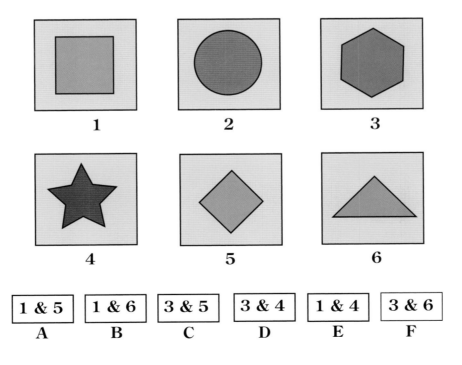

1   2   3

4   5   6

1 & 5	1 & 6	3 & 5	3 & 4	1 & 4	3 & 6
A	B	C	D	E	F

3.

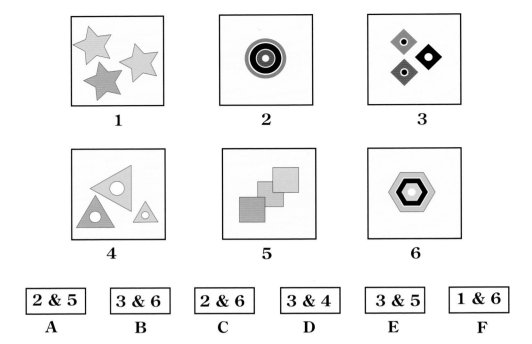

2 & 5	3 & 6	2 & 6	3 & 4	3 & 5	1 & 6
A	B	C	D	E	F

4.

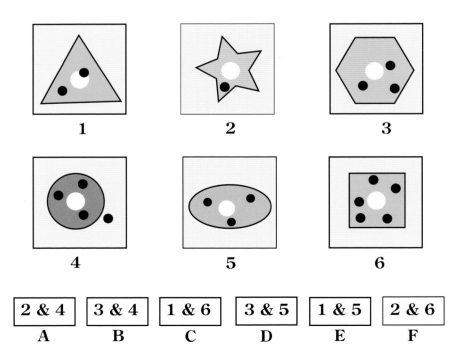

2 & 4	3 & 4	1 & 6	3 & 5	1 & 5	2 & 6
A	B	C	D	E	F

5.

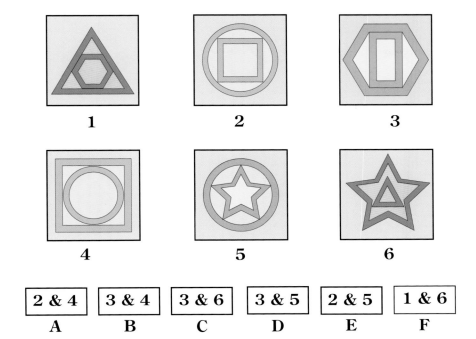

2 & 4	3 & 4	3 & 6	3 & 5	2 & 5	1 & 6
A	B	C	D	E	F

6.

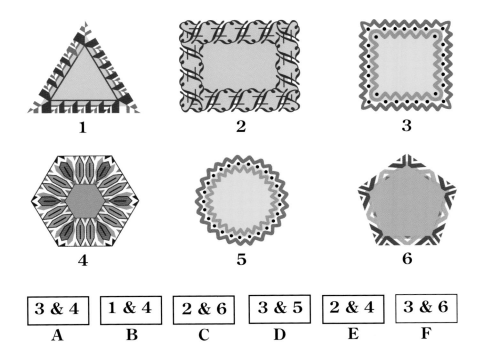

3 & 4	1 & 4	2 & 6	3 & 5	2 & 4	3 & 6
A	B	C	D	E	F

7.

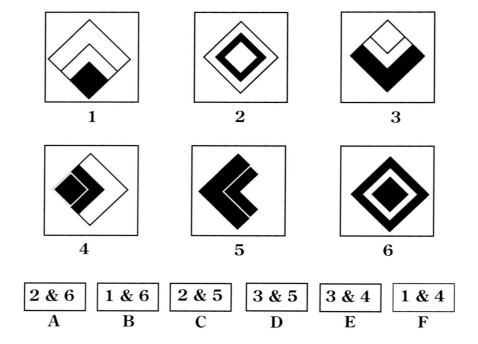

2 & 6	1 & 6	2 & 5	3 & 5	3 & 4	1 & 4
A	**B**	**C**	**D**	**E**	**F**

8.

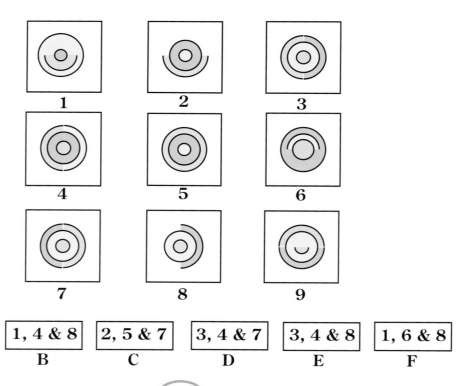

2, 5 & 9	1, 4 & 8	2, 5 & 7	3, 4 & 7	3, 4 & 8	1, 6 & 8
A	**B**	**C**	**D**	**E**	**F**

9.

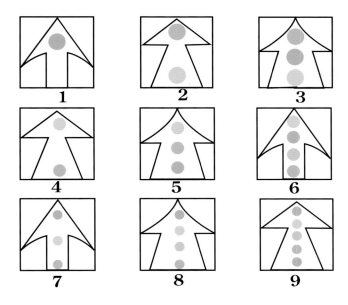

2, 5 & 9	1, 5 & 7	3, 5 & 7	3, 4 & 7	2, 4 & 8	1,6 & 7
A	B	C	D	E	F

10.

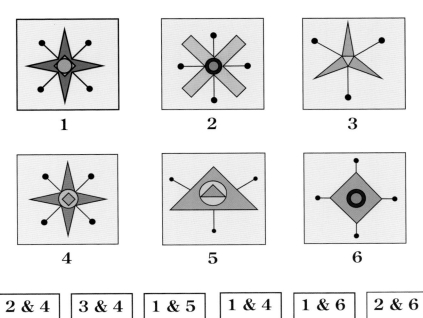

2 & 4	3 & 4	1 & 5	1 & 4	1 & 6	2 & 6
A	B	C	D	E	F

11.

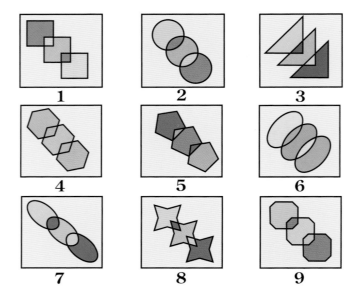

2, 5 & 8	2, 6 & 7	2, 5 & 9	1, 4 & 9	3, 4 & 8	1, 6 & 8
A	B	C	D	E	F

12.

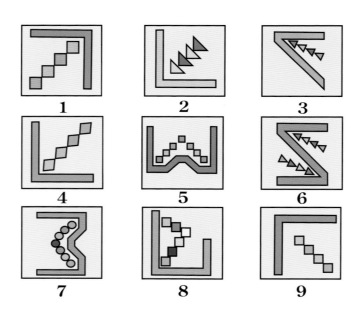

2, 5 & 7	3, 6 & 7	2, 6 & 9	1, 4 & 8	1, 4 & 9	1, 6 & 9
A	B	C	D	E	F

13.

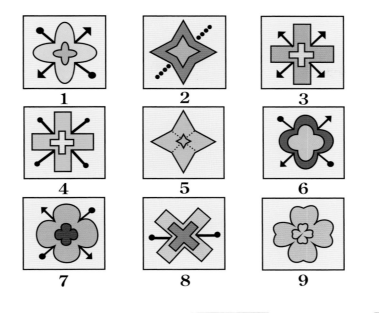

1, 6 & 7	2, 5 & 7	2, 6 & 7	3, 4 & 8	2, 4 & 9	1, 5 & 9
A	B	C	D	E	F

14.

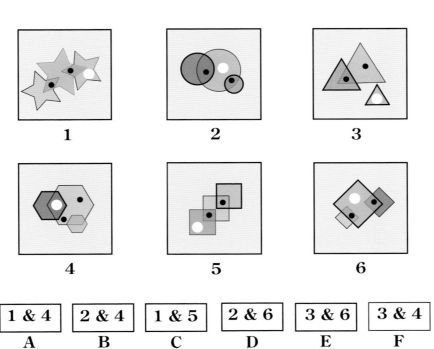

1 & 4	2 & 4	1 & 5	2 & 6	3 & 6	3 & 4
A	B	C	D	E	F

15.

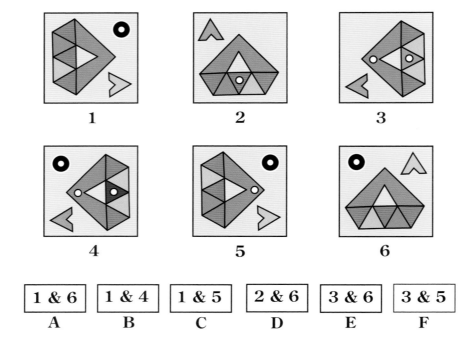

1 & 6	1 & 4	1 & 5	2 & 6	3 & 6	3 & 5
A	B	C	D	E	F

16.

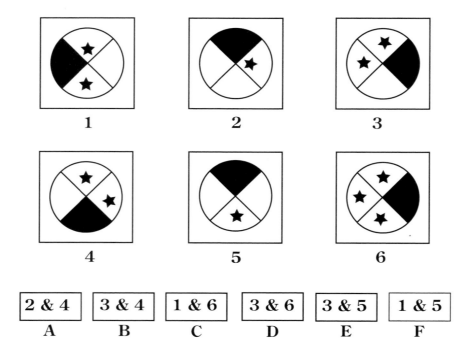

2 & 4	3 & 4	1 & 6	3 & 6	3 & 5	1 & 5
A	B	C	D	E	F

17.

 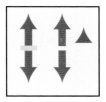

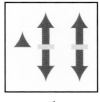

1   2   3

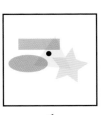 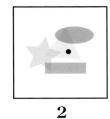 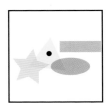

4   5   6

2 & 4	2 & 5	1 & 5	2 & 6	3 & 5	3 & 4
A	B	C	D	E	F

18.

1   2   3

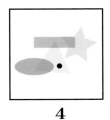 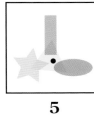 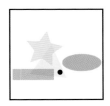

4   5   6

3 & 5	1 & 6	1 & 5	2 & 6	3 & 4	3 & 6
A	B	C	D	E	F

19.

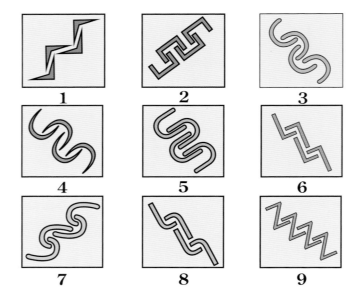

1, 6 & 8	2, 5 & 7	2, 6 & 8	3, 5 & 8	2, 4 & 9	3, 5 & 7
A	B	C	D	E	F

20.

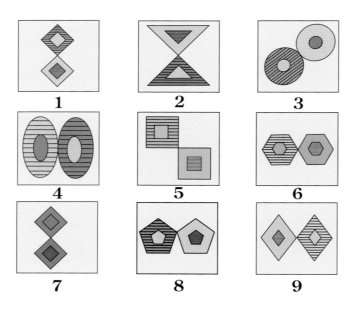

2, 6 & 8	1, 5 & 9	1, 6 & 7	3, 5 & 7	3, 4 & 9	2, 5 & 7
A	B	C	D	E	F

21.

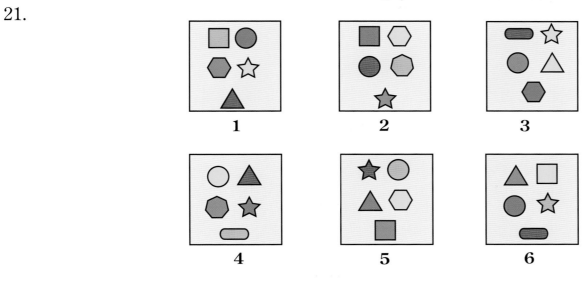

1	2	3
4	5	6

2 & 5	1 & 4	3 & 5	1 & 5	3 & 4	2 & 6
A	B	C	D	E	F

22.

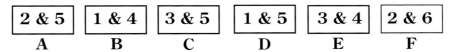

1	2	3
4	5	6

1 & 6	1 & 5	2 & 4	1 & 4	3 & 6	3 & 5
A	B	C	D	E	F

23.

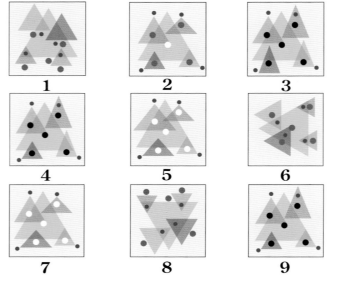

1	2	3
4	5	6
7	8	9

3, 4 & 8	3, 6 & 9	2, 6 & 7	2, 5 & 9	1, 6 & 8	1, 5 & 9
A	B	C	D	E	F

24.

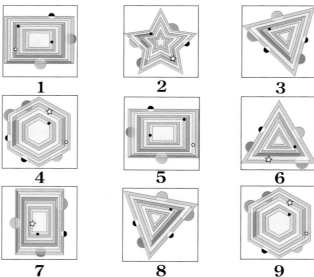

1	2	3
4	5	6
7	8	9

1, 6 & 8	2, 5 & 9	3, 4 & 7	3, 6 & 7	1, 5 & 9	2, 6 & 7
A	B	C	D	E	F

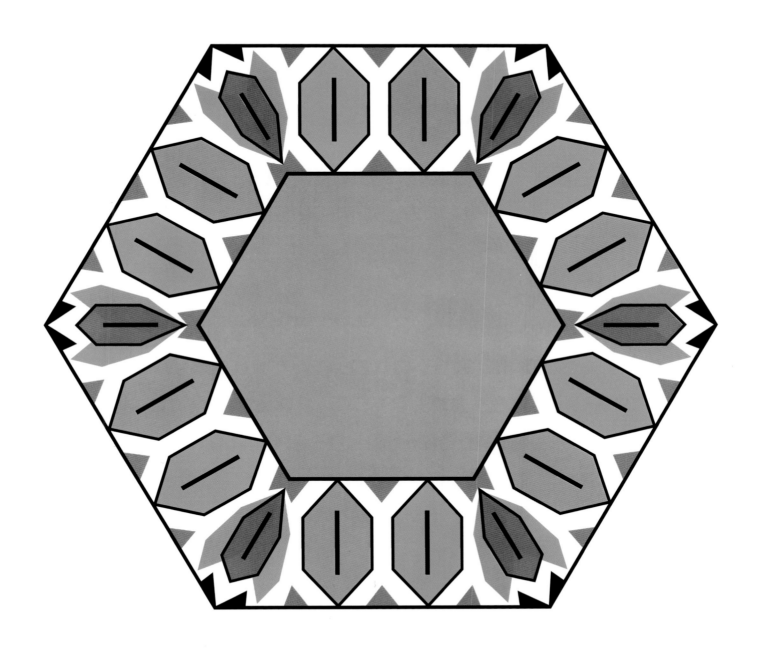

BRICKS

- In each of the puzzles that follow, the cut-shapes are to be fitted in the given grid. These cut-shapes can be rotated in any angle, however no cut-shape can be repeated, changed or reversed.
- Find the correct answer from the options given.

1.

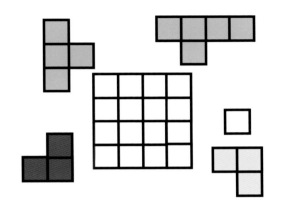
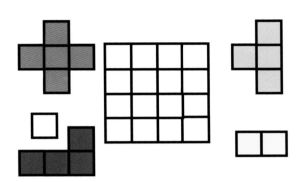

A
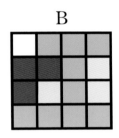

B
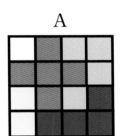

C
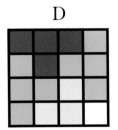

D
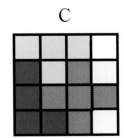

2.

A

B

C

D

3.

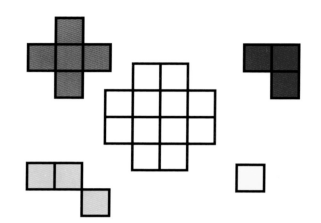 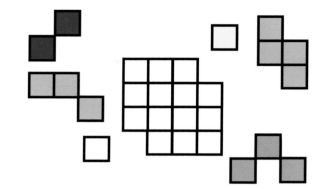

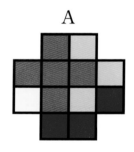 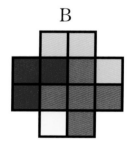 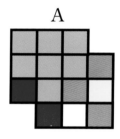

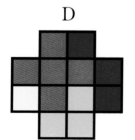 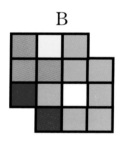

A

B

C

D

4.

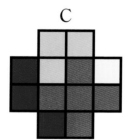 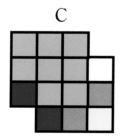 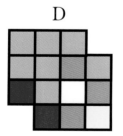

A

B

C

D

5.

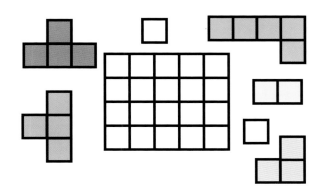

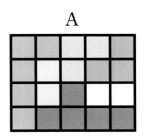

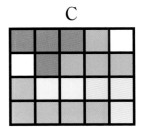

A

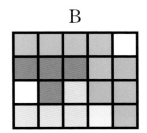

B

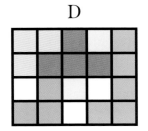

C

D

6.

A

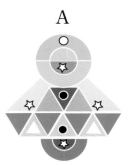

B

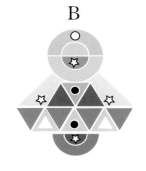

C

D

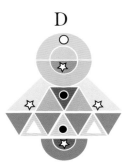

7.

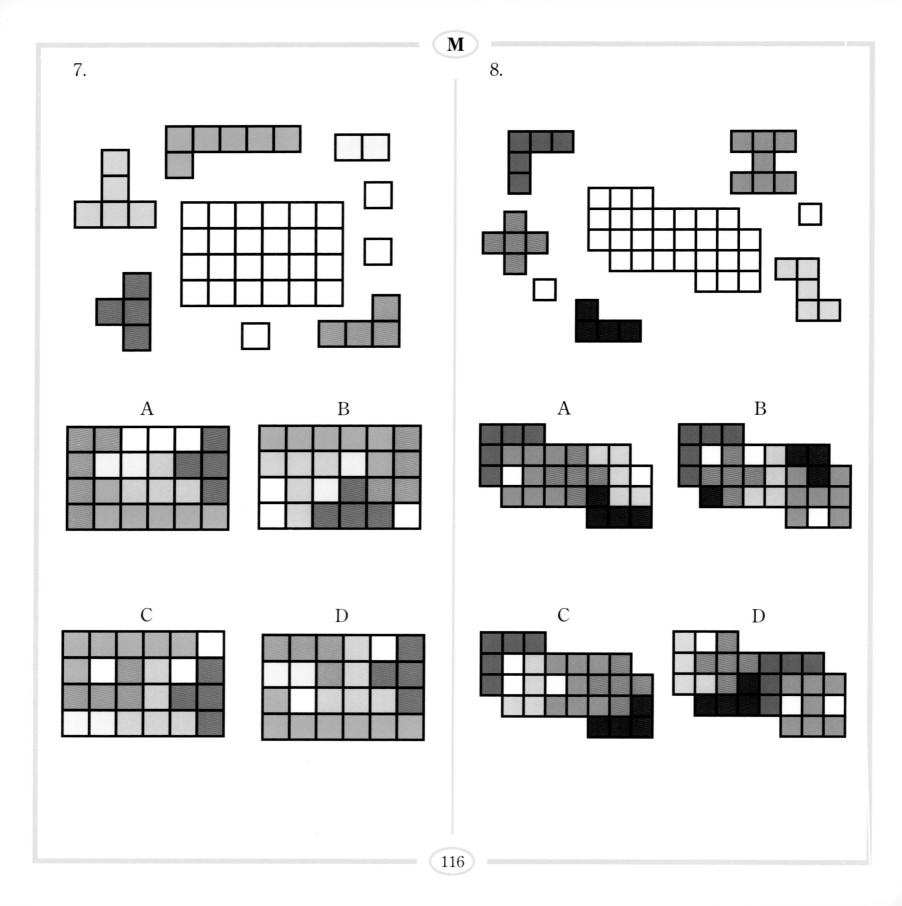

A

B

C

D

8.

9.

A

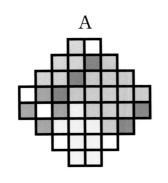

B

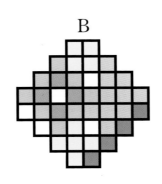

C

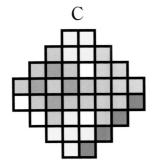

D

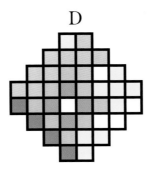

10.

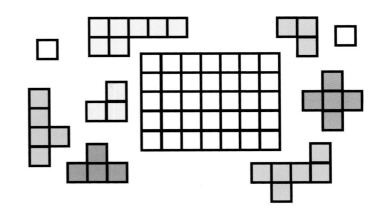

A

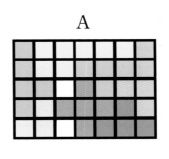

B

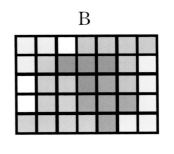

C

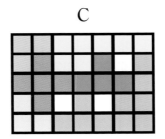

D

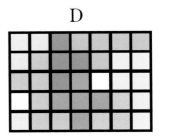

11.

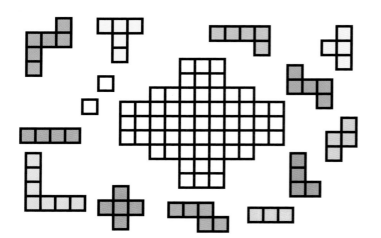

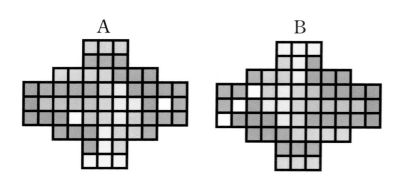

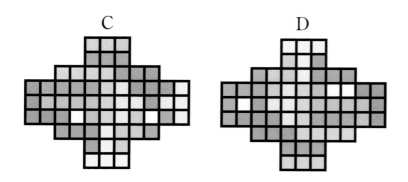

A

B

C

D

12.

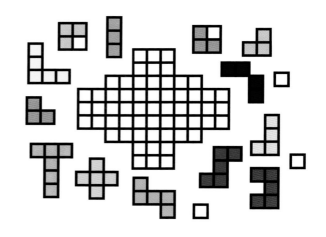

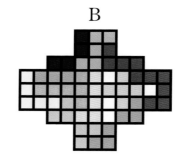

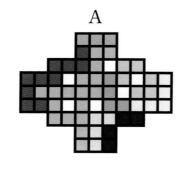

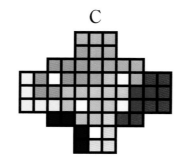

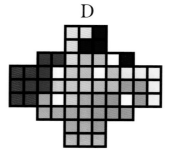

A

B

C

D

13.

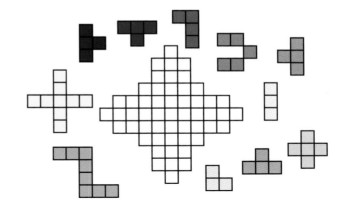

A

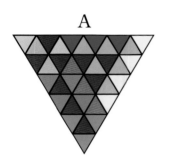

B

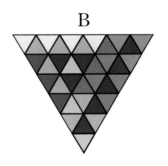

A

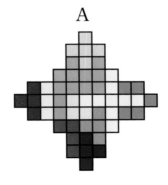

B

C

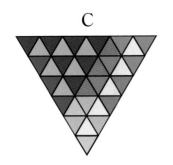

D

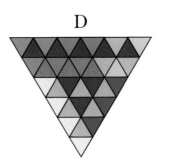

C

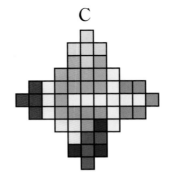

D

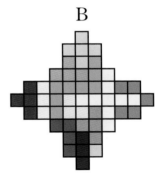

14.

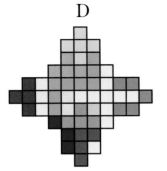

15.

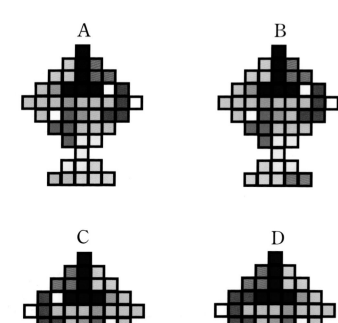

16.

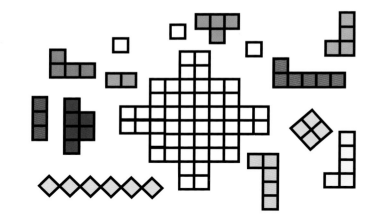

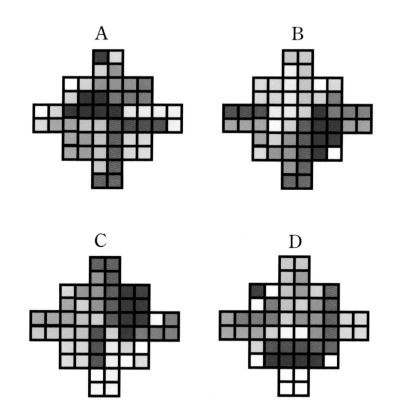

17.

18.

A

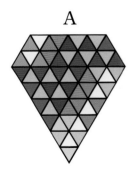

B

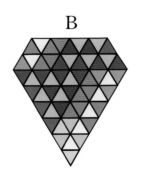

A

B

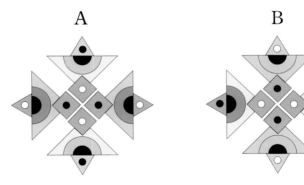

C

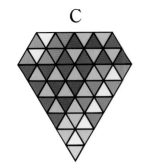

D

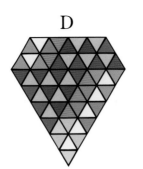

C

D

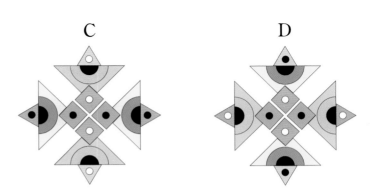

19.

A

B

C

D

20.

A

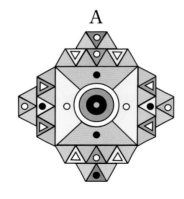

B

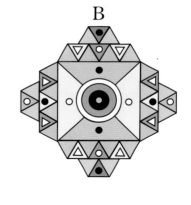

C

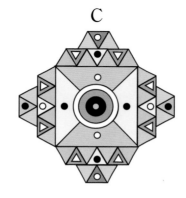

D

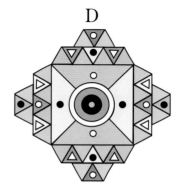

21.

A

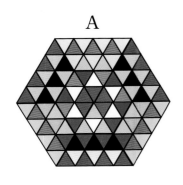

22.

B

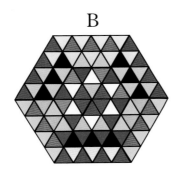

A

B

C

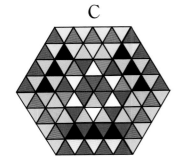

A

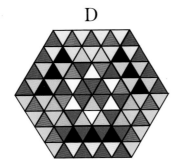

B

D

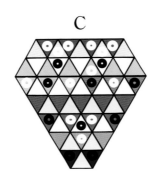

C

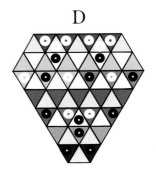

D

23.

A

B

C

D

24.

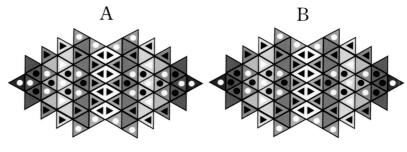

A

B

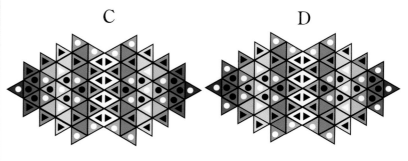

C

D

25.

26.

A B

C D

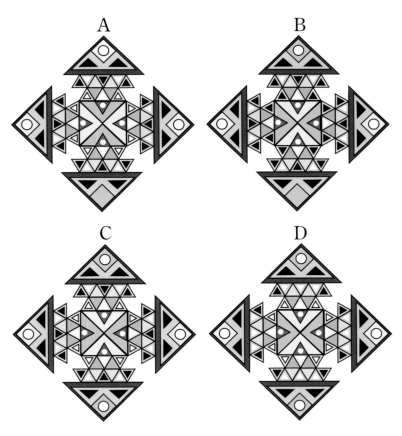

A B

C D

COLOR PERCEPTION

- In this category you would have to reason with colors. The problem figure is a complete figure with four answer options. Only one answer option is an identical 'part' of the 'whole' problem figure. You have to find this option.

1.

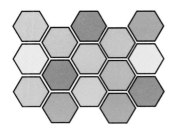

   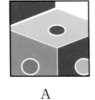

A   B   C   D

2.

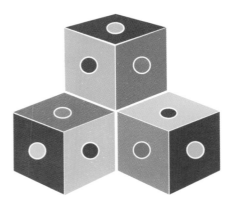

A   B   C   D

3.

  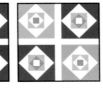

A   B   C   D

4.

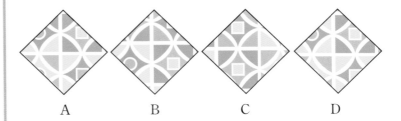

A   B   C   D

5.

A   B   C   D

6.

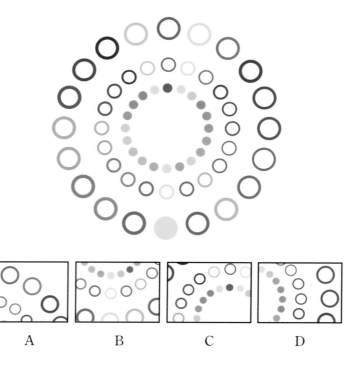

A   B   C   D

7.

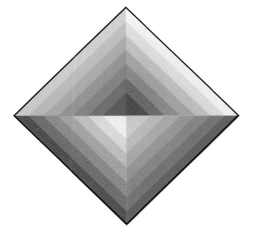

A   B   C   D

8.

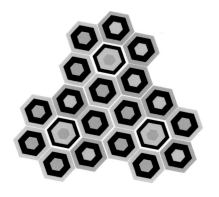

A   B   C   D

9.

A   B   C   D

10.

A   B   C   D

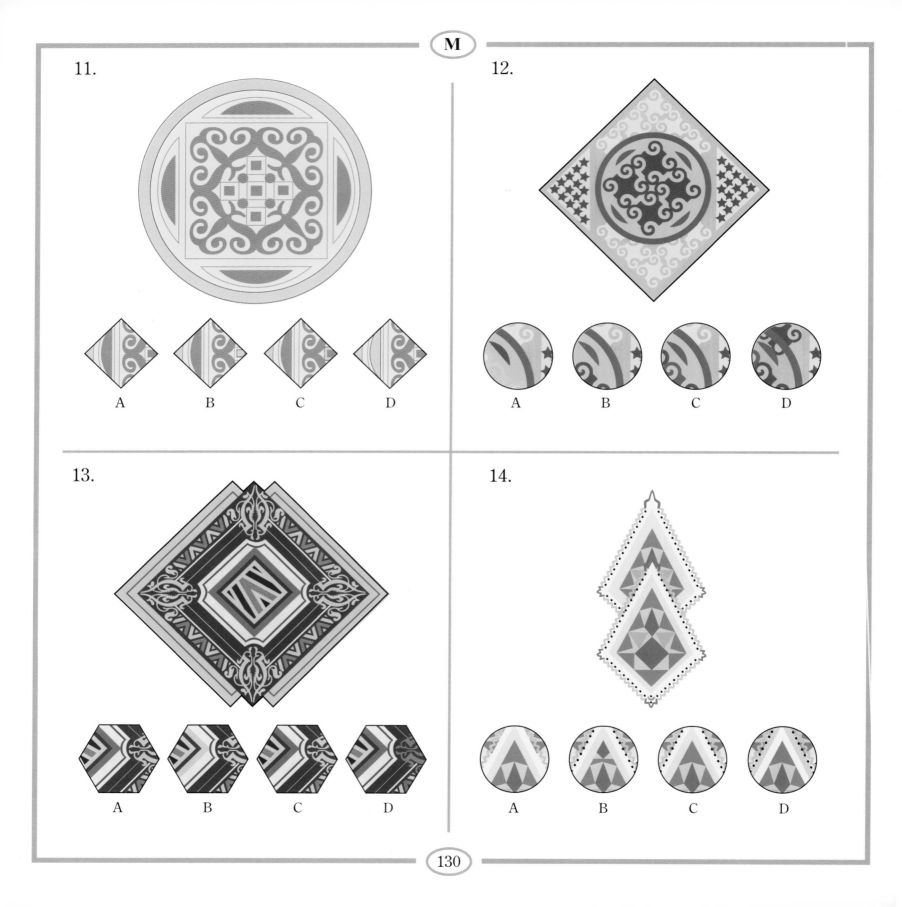

11.

A B C D

12.

A B C D

13.

A B C D

14.

A B C D

15.

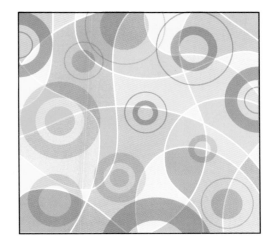

A   B   C   D

16.

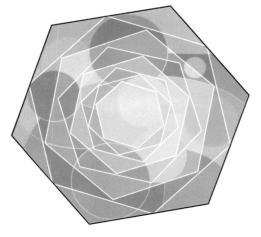

A   B   C   D

17.

A   B   C   D

18.

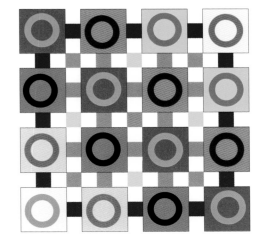

A   B   C   D

19.

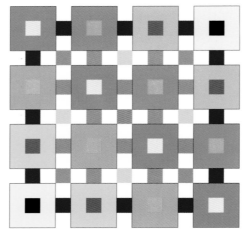

A   B   C   D

20.

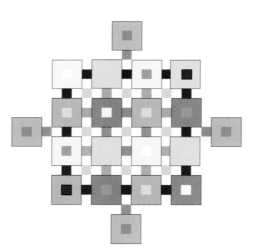

A   B   C   D

21.

A   B   C   D

22.

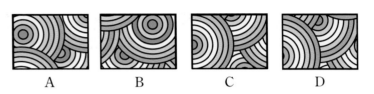

A   B   C   D

23.

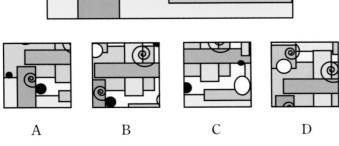

A   B   C   D

24.

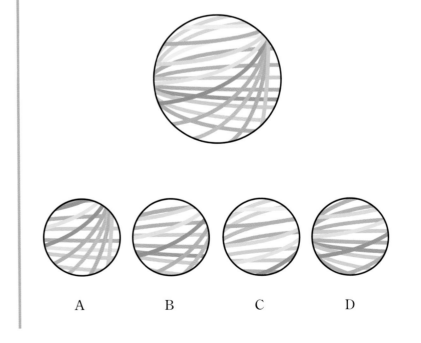

A   B   C   D

25.

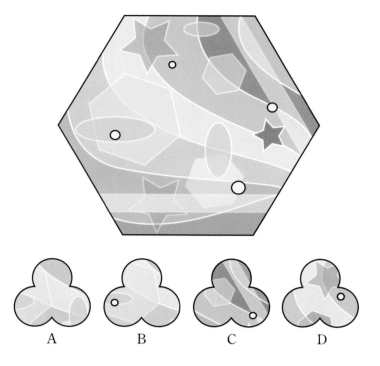

A   B   C   D

26.

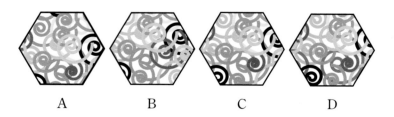

A   B   C   D

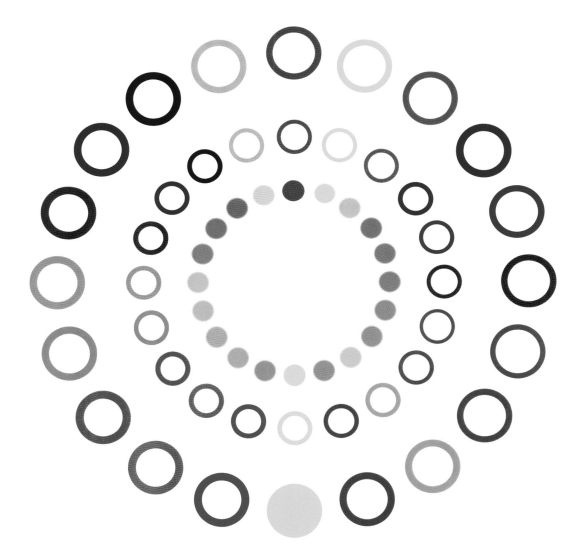

MATRIX

- One piece from each of the matrices is missing.
- To complete each matrix, choose the most appropriate option from the choices given.

1.

A

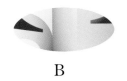

B

C

D

2.

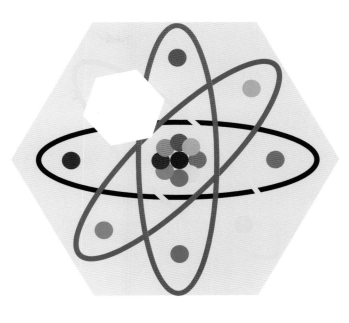

A

B

C

D

3.

A

B

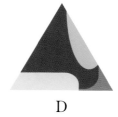
C

D

4.

A

B

C

D

5.

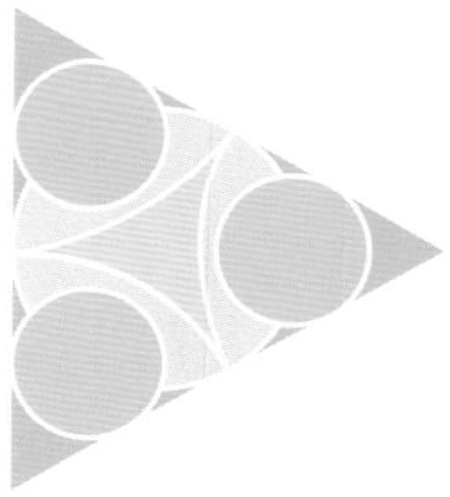

A

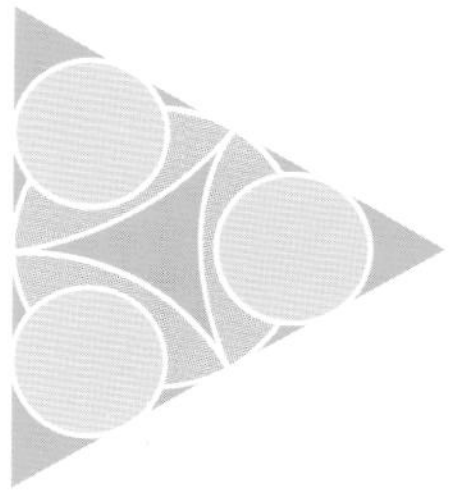

B

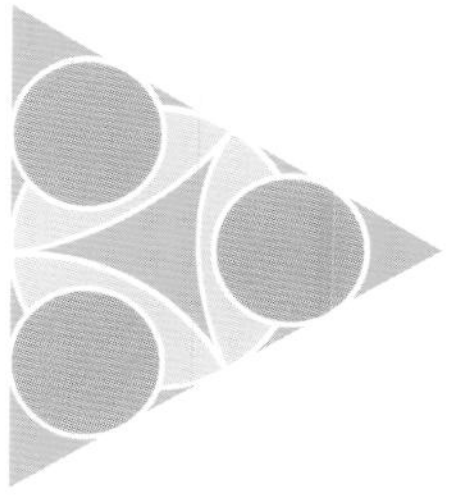

C

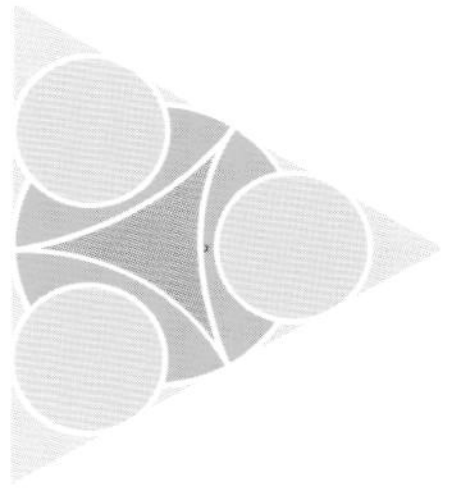

D

6.

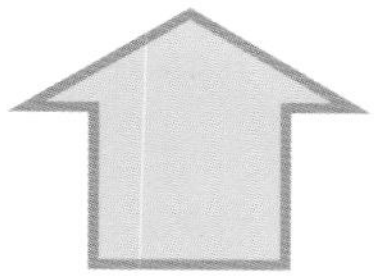

A

B

C

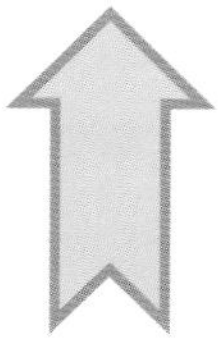

D

7.

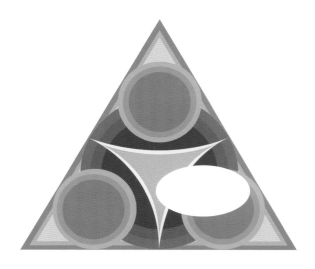

A

B

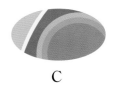

C

D

8.

A

B

C

D

9.

1 2 3 4 5 6 7 8 9 10

A   B

A   B

C   D

10.

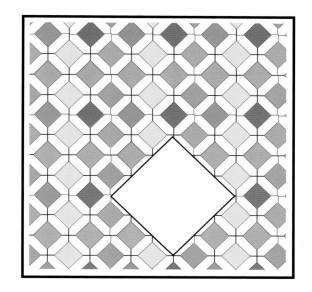

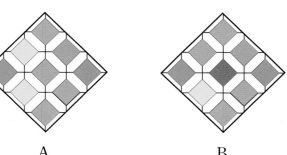

A   B

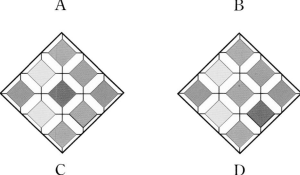

C   D

11.

A

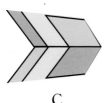

B

C

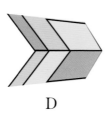

D

12.

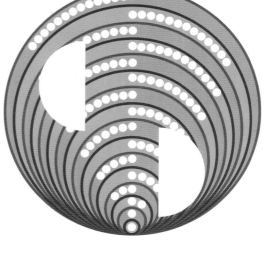

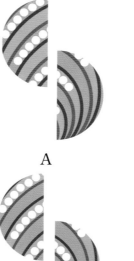

A

B

C

D

13.

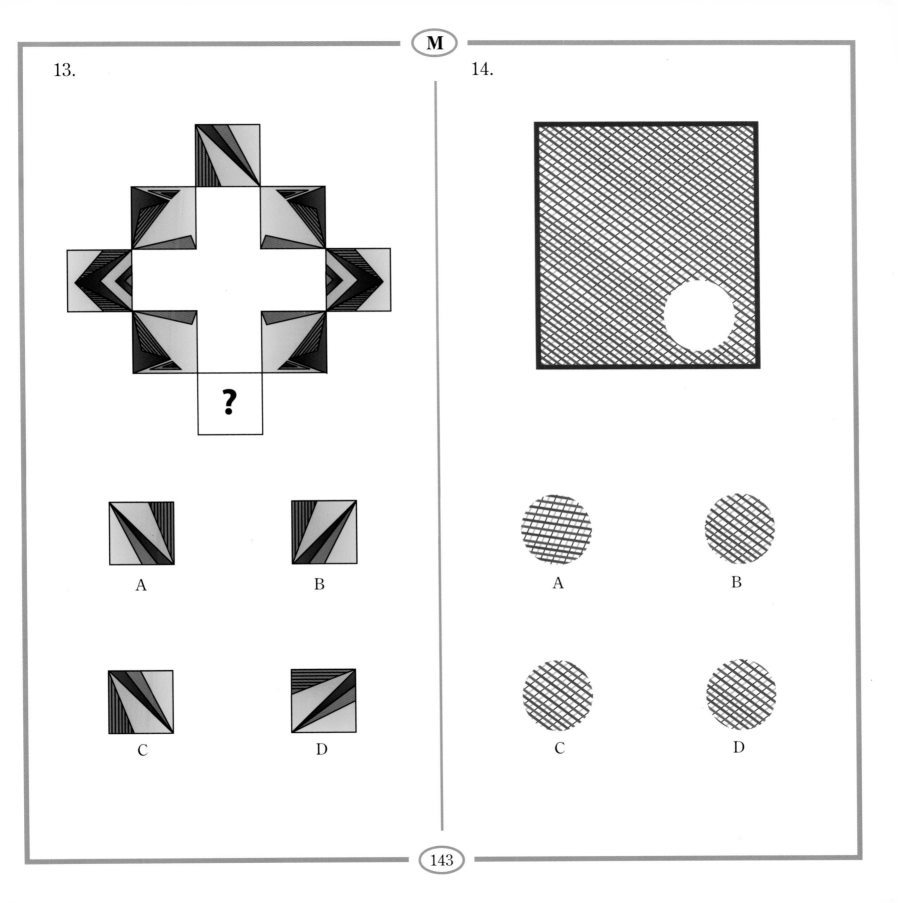

A

B

C

D

14.

A

B

C

D

15.

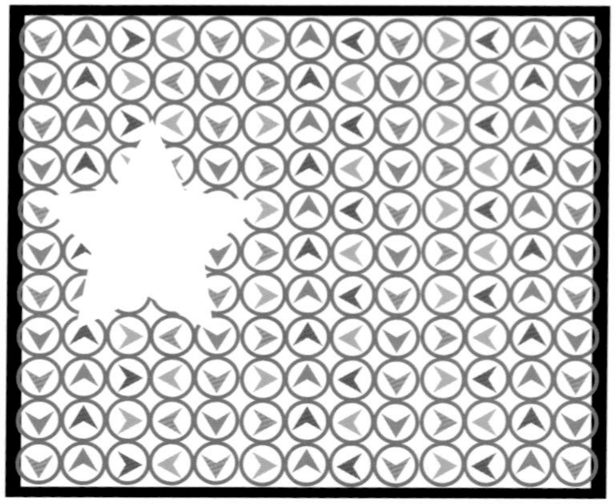

A

B

C

D

16.

A

B

C

D

17.

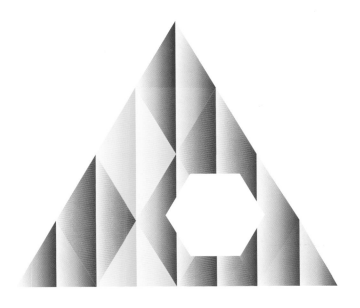

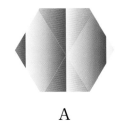

A

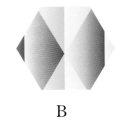

B

C

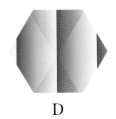

D

18.

A   B

C   D

19.

A

B

C

D

20.

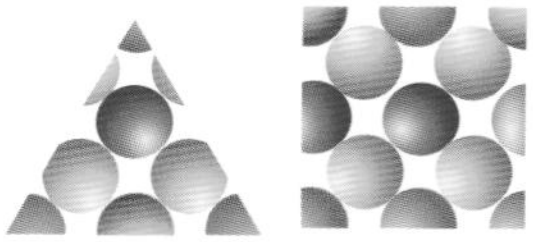

A

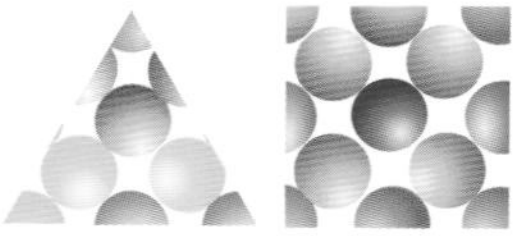

B

C

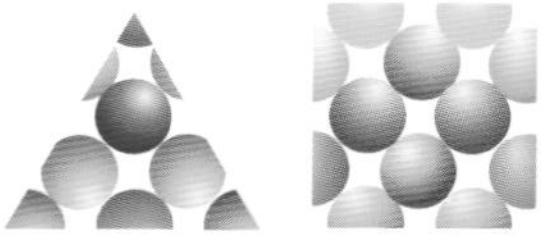

D

21.

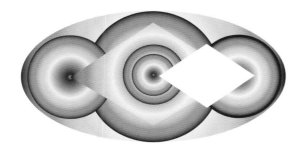

A

B

C

D

22.

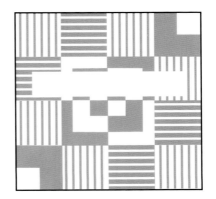

A   B

C   D

23.

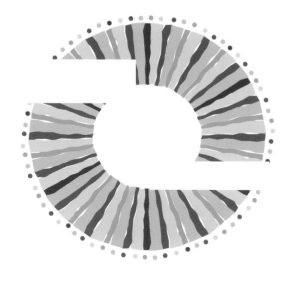

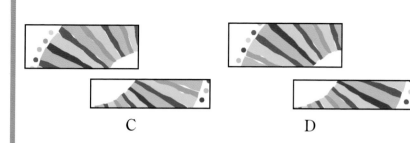

A   B

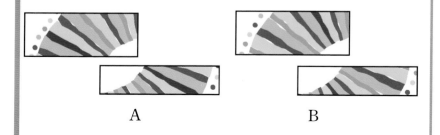

C   D

24.

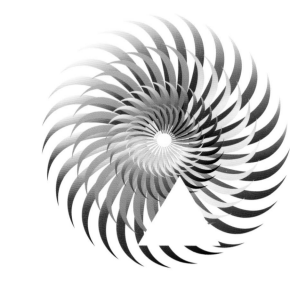

A   B

C   D

25.

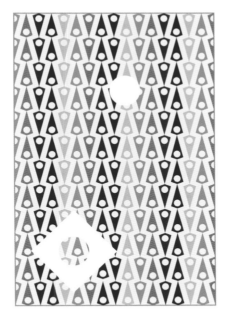

A

B

C

D

26.

A

B

C

D

WORD POWER

- Each puzzle in this section has specific instructions.
- Read each question carefully before you solve the puzzle.
- Try solving puzzles in the easy and medium category in two minutes, and puzzles in the difficult category in one minute.

1.
Unscramble the letters to get a 12 letter word. Make as many 3 - 12 letter words from the letters given below. Remember each word can use a letter only once.

V A G T
A A R N
E A Z X

2.
Unscramble the letters to get a 12 letter word. Make as many 4 - 12 letter words from the letters given below. Remember each word can use a letter only once.

B U T C
S E R S
L U O I

3.
Unscramble the letters to get a 15 letter word. Make as many 4 - 15 letter words from the letters given below. Remember each word can use a letter only once.

L N M
O E R A I
C E C T T E
G

4.
Unscramble the letters to get a 12 letter word. Make as many 4 - 12 letter words from the letters given below. Remember each word can use a letter only once.

L P D A C
I Y E C
N O E

5.
Unscramble the letters to get a 10 letter word. Make as many 3 - 10 letter words from the letters given below. Remember each word can use a letter only once.

S P Y G
H L O
O Y I

6.
Unscramble the letters to get a 10 letter word. Make as many 3 - 10 letter words from the letters given below. Remember each word can use a letter only once.

S M
M E N
T R A
I D

7.
How many words of 4 or more letters can you make from the letters shown? Each word can use a letter only once and must contain the central letter.
There should be one 9 letter word.

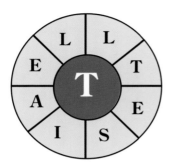

8.
How many words of 4 or more letters can you make from the letters shown? Each word can use a letter only once and must contain the central letter.
There should be one 9 letter word.

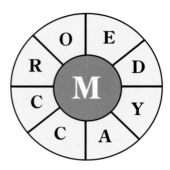

9.
How many words of 3 or more letters can you make from the letters shown? Each word can use a letter only once and must contain the central letter.
There should be one 8 letter word.

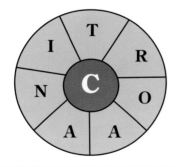

10.
How many words of 4 or more letters can you make from the letters shown? Each word can use a letter only once and must contain the central letter.
There should be one 8 letter word.

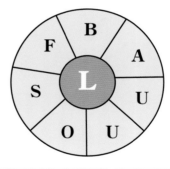

11.
How many words of 3 or more letters can you make from the letters shown? Each word can use a letter only once and must contain the central letter.
There should be one 7 letter word.

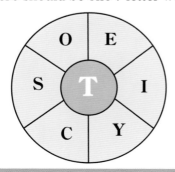

12.
How many words of 4 or more letters can you make from the letters shown? Each word can use a letter only once and must contain the central letter.
There should be one 14 letter word.

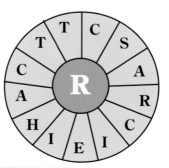

13.

How many words of 4 or more letters can you make from the letters shown? Each word can use a letter only once and must contain the central letter. There should be one 12 letter word.

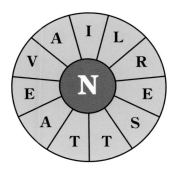

14.

How many words of 3 or more letters can you make from the letters shown? Each word can use a letter only once and must contain the central letter. There should be one 9 letter word.

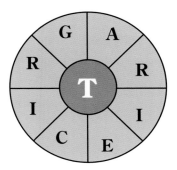

15.

How many words of 4 or more letters can you make from the letters shown? Each word can use a letter only once and must contain the central letter. There should be one 10 letter word.

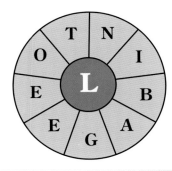

16.

How many words of 3 or more letters can you make from the letters shown? Each word can use a letter only once and must contain the central letter. There should be one 10 letter word.

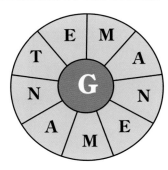

17.

How many words of 3 or more letters can you make from the letters shown? Each word can use a letter only once and must contain the central letter. There should be one 10 letter word.

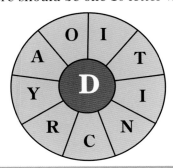

18.

How many words of 4 or more letters can you make from the letters shown? Each word can use a letter only once and must contain the central letter. There should be one 9 letter word.

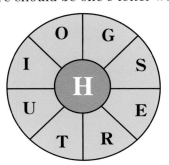

19.

How many words of 4 or more letters can you make
from the letters shown? Each word can use a letter
only once and must contain the central letter.
There should be one 12 letter word.

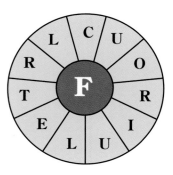

20.

How many words of 3 or more letters can you make
from the letters shown? Each word can use a letter
only once and must contain the central letter.
There should be one 9 letter word.

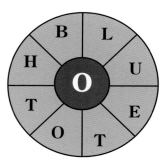

21.

How many words of 4 or more letters can you make from the letters shown? Each word can use a letter only once and must contain the central letter. There should be one 14 letter word.

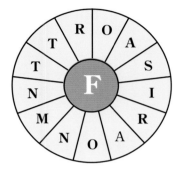

22.

How many words of 4 or more letters can you make from the letters shown? Each word can use a letter only once and must contain the central letter. There should be one 11 letter word.

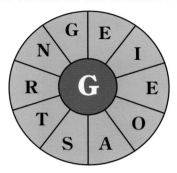

23.

How many words of 3 or more letters can you make from the letters shown? Each word can use a letter only once and must contain the central letter. There should be one 7 letter word.

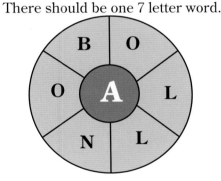

24.

How many words of 3 or more letters can you make from the letters shown? Each word can use a letter only once and must contain the central letter. There should be one 8 letter word.

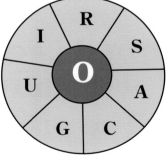

25.

How many words of 4 or more letters can you make from the letters shown? Each word can use a letter only once and must contain the central letter. There should be one 14 letter word.

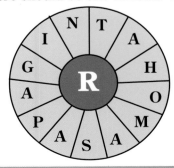

26.

How many words of 3 or more letters can you make from the letters shown? Each word can use a letter only once and must contain the central letter. There should be one 7 letter word.

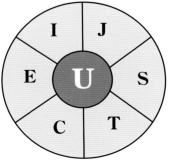

SPACE PERCEPTION

- In this category, you will be dealing with three dimensional figures.
- The problem figure can be folded to form a three dimensional figure.
- You have to decide which one of the answer figures can be made by folding the problem figure.
- There is only one right answer.

1.

2.

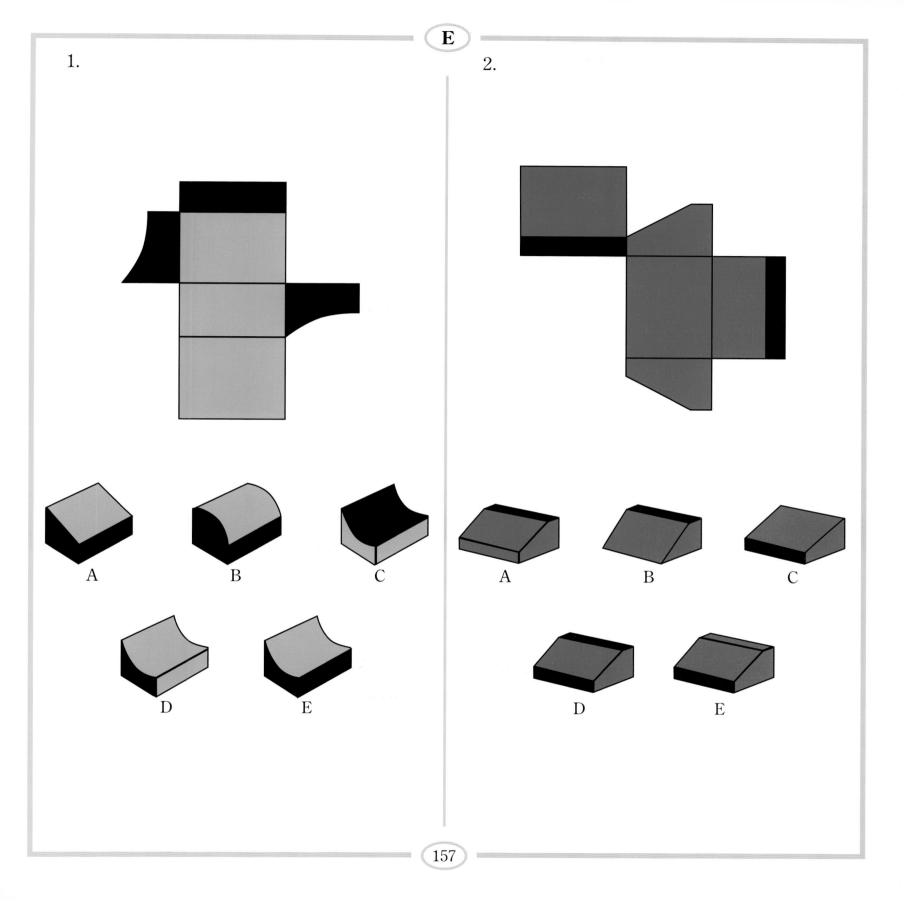

A   B   C

D   E

A   B   C

D   E

3.

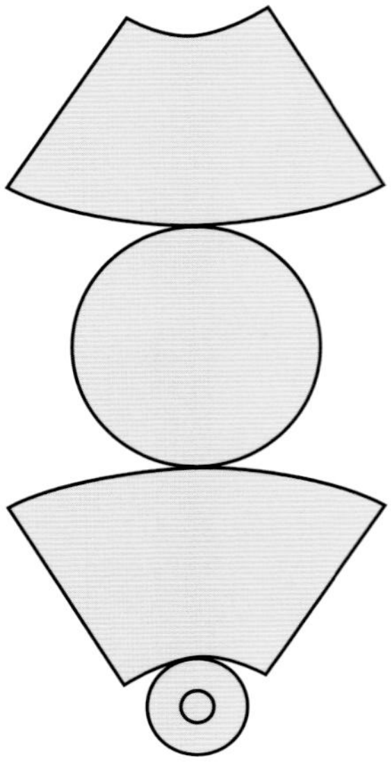

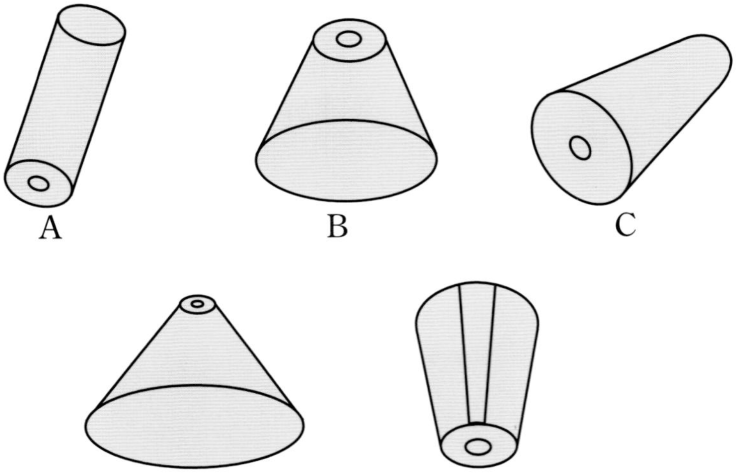

A B C

D E

4.

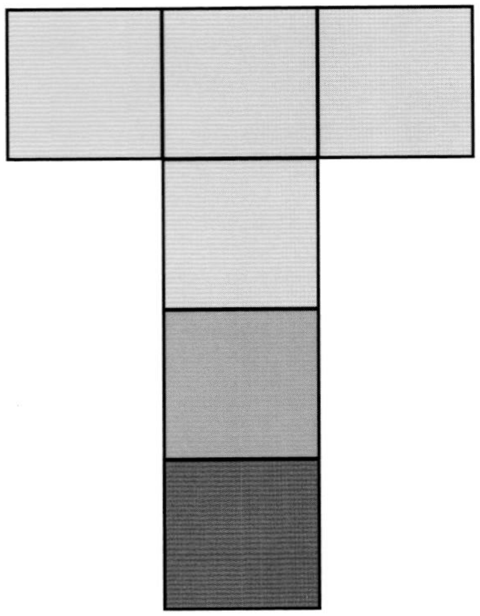

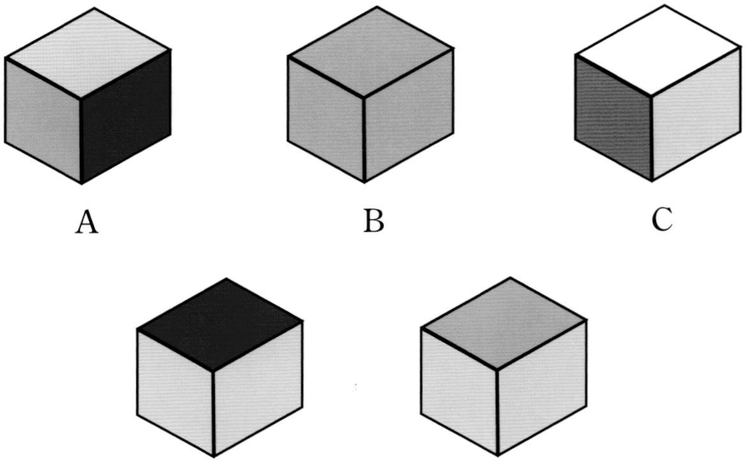

A B C

D E

5.

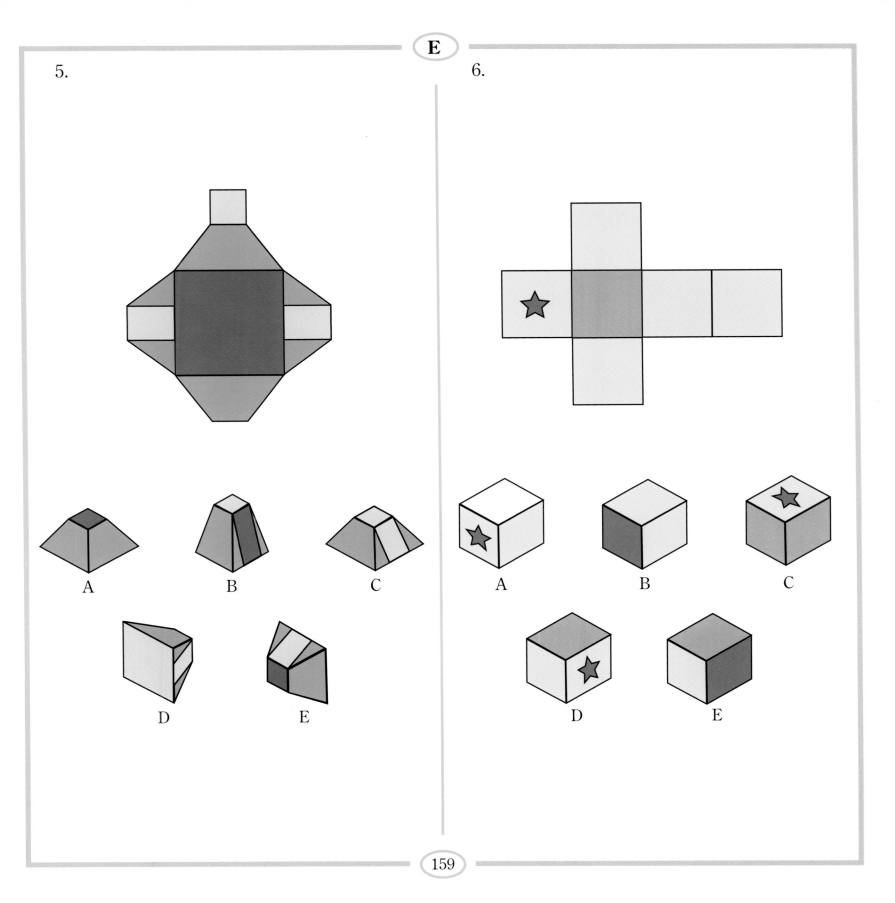

A

B

C

D

E

6.

A

B

C

D

E

7.

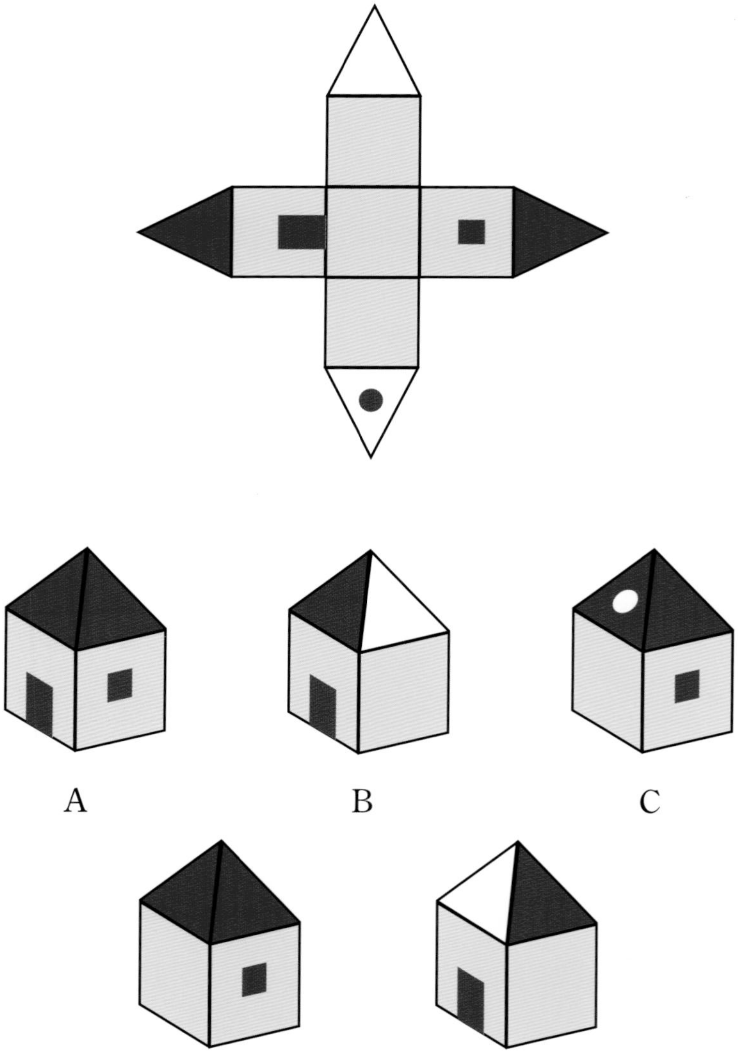

A   B   C

D   E

8.

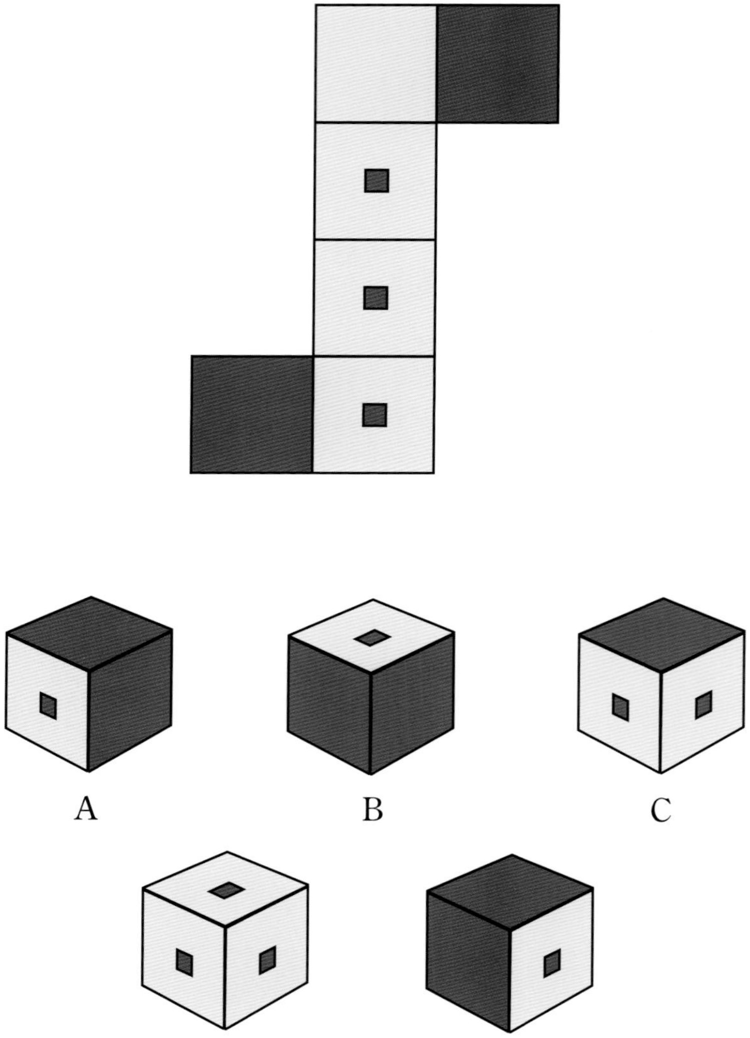

A   B   C

D   E

9.

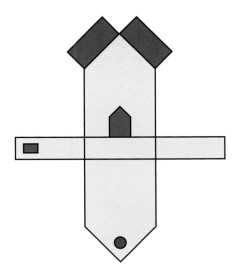

A

B

C

D

E

10.

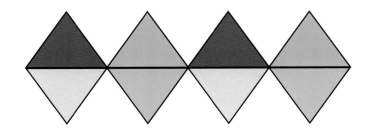

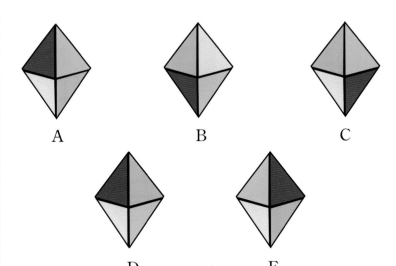

A

B

C

D

E

11.

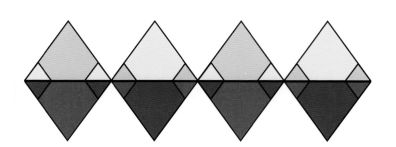

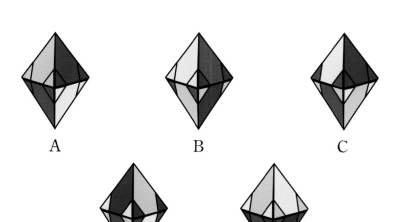

A   B   C

D   E

12.

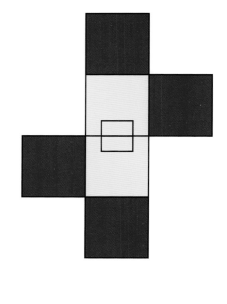

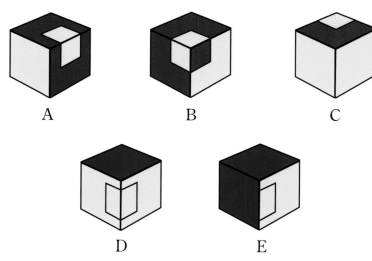

A   B   C

D   E

13.

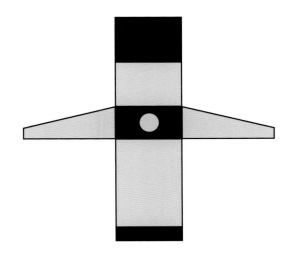

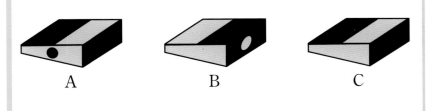

A   B   C

D   E

14.

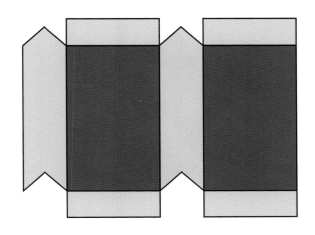

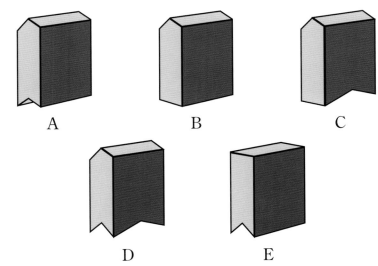

A   B   C

D   E

15.

A

B

C

D

E

16.

A

B

C

D

E

17.

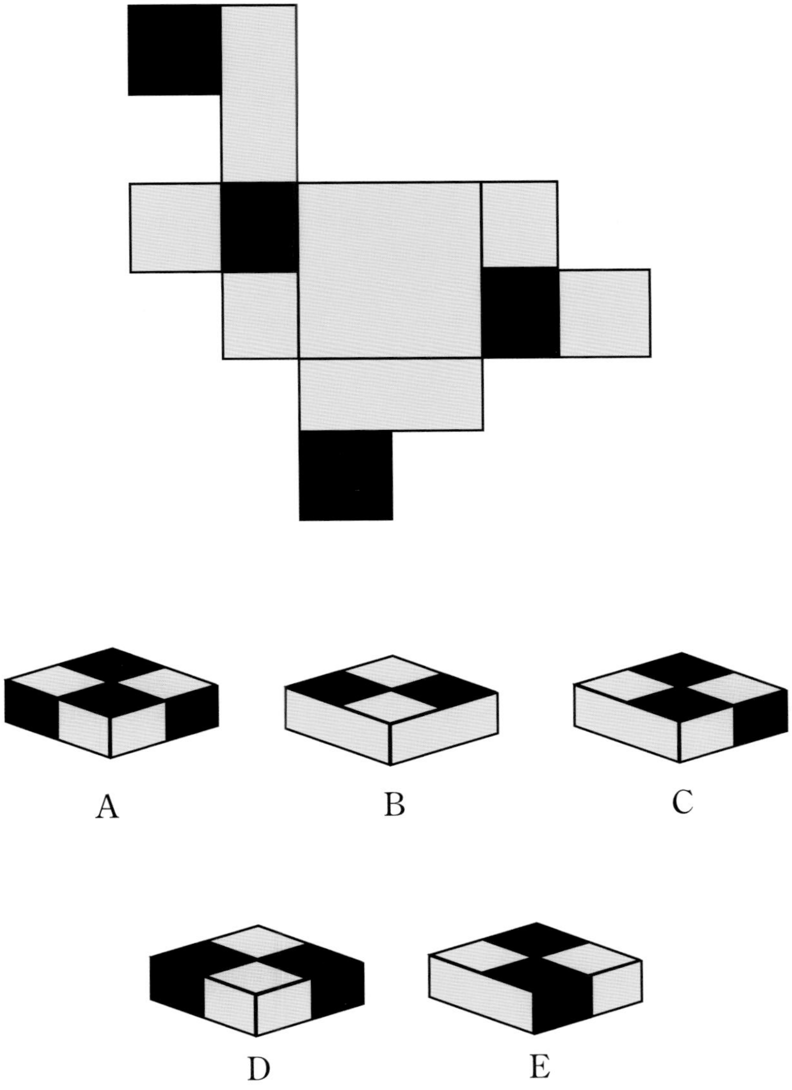

A

B

C

D

E

18.

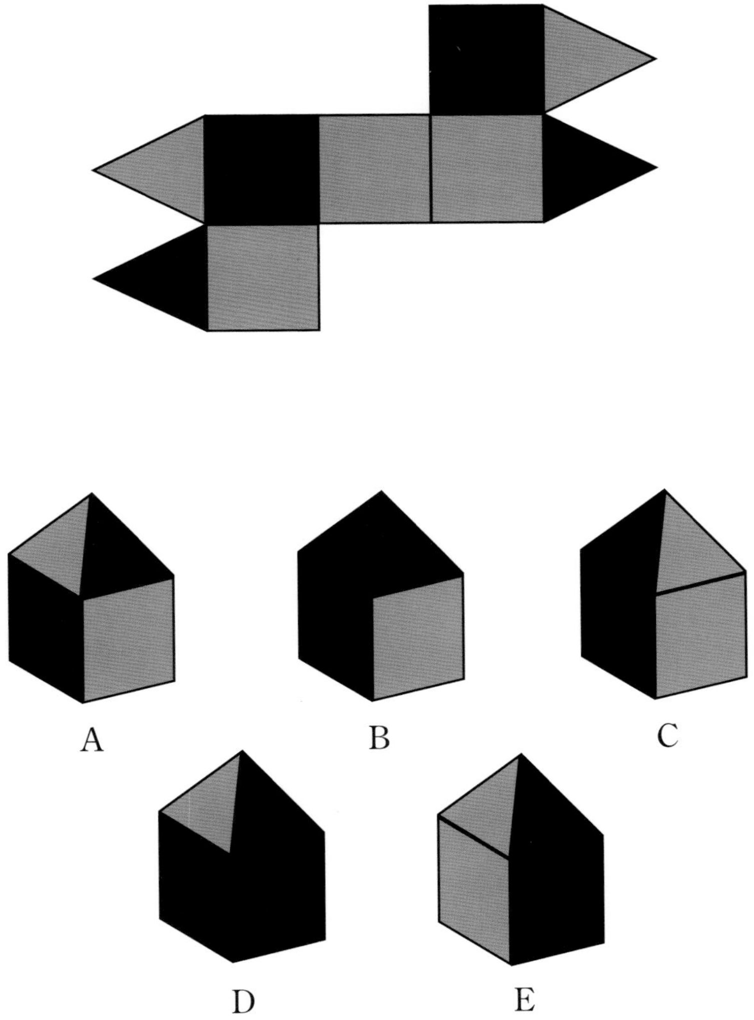

A

B

C

D

E

19.

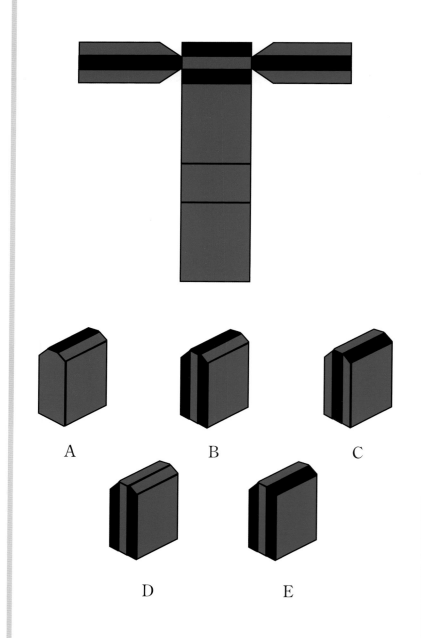

A   B   C

D   E

20.

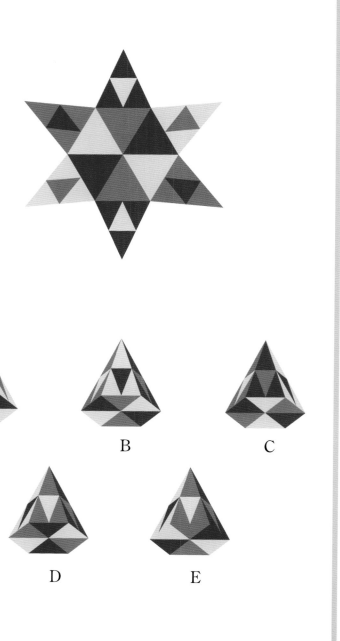

A   B   C

D   E

21.

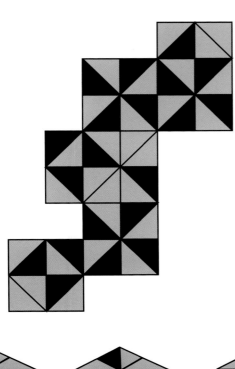

A B C

D E

22.

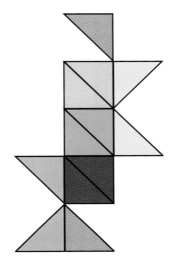

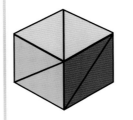 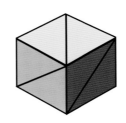 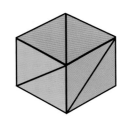

A B C

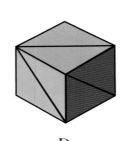 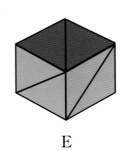

D E

23.

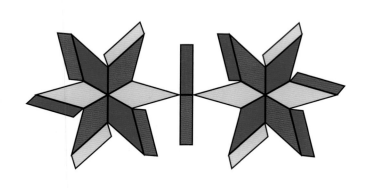

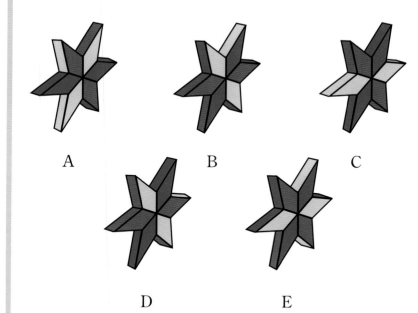

A   B   C

D   E

24.

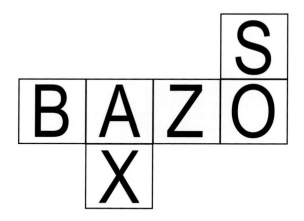

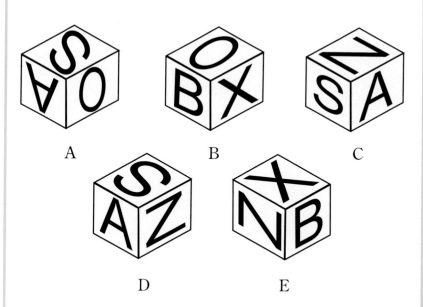

A   B   C

D   E

25.

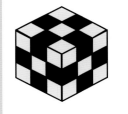  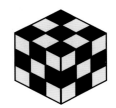

A   B   C

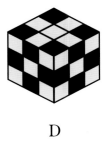 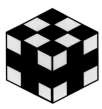

D   E

26.

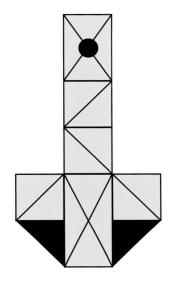

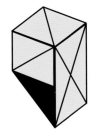 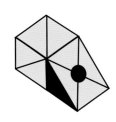 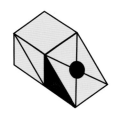

A   B   C

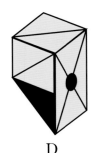 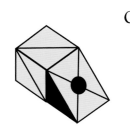

D   E

CLUSTER

- **In the series of puzzles that are to follow, instructions would differ from puzzle to puzzle.**
- **Read each question carefully before you solve the puzzle.**

1.

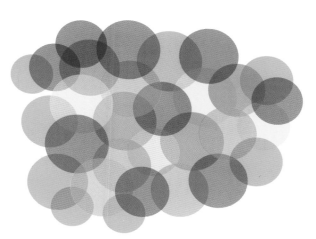

- How many blue circles intersect orange circles?

8	5	4	6
A	B	C	D

2.

- Count the number of ten sided stars.

10	12	14	17
A	B	C	D

3.

- Find the total number of blue triangles.

5	8	7	4
A	B	C	D

4.

- Find the number of squares with rounded corners.

14	13	7	15
A	B	C	D

5.

- **Find how many dots are in the center of the shape.**

9	8	12	16
A	B	C	D

6.

- **Find the total number of small triangles.**

15	18	10	12
A	B	C	D

7.

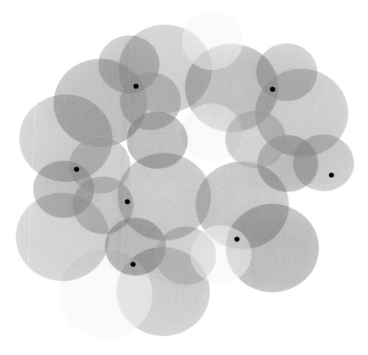

- **Find the number of circles containing a black dot.**

10	**7**	**9**	**19**
A	B	C	D

8.

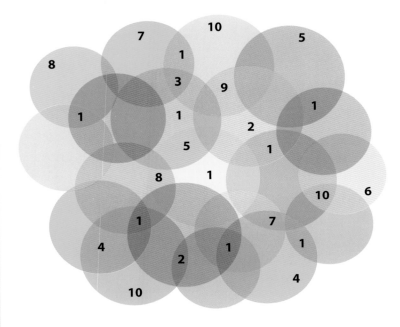

- **Find the total number of circles containing the digit 1.**

12	**19**	**22**	**21**
A	B	C	D

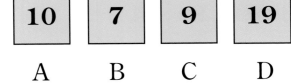

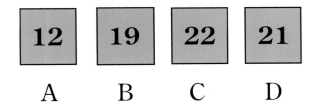

9.

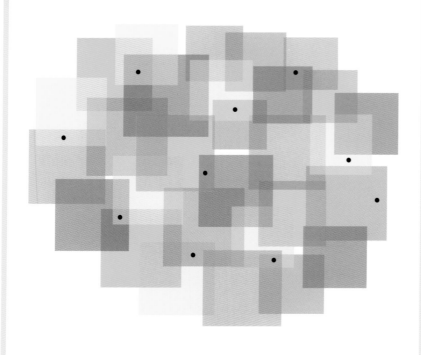

• **Find the number of big squares which do not contain a black dot.**

6	**9**	**8**	**21**
A	B	C	D

10.

• **Find the number of big squares which do not intersect circles.**

10	**9**	**15**	**8**
A	B	C	D

11.

• **Find the number of pentagons.**

3	9	7	5
A	B	C	D

12.

• **Find the number of green stars intersecting pink and blue stars.**

6	11	7	8
A	B	C	D

13.

14.

• **Find the number of diamonds containing a black dot.**

10	17	20	16
A	B	C	D

• **Find the number of squares intersecting orange circles.**

21	19	20	22
A	B	C	D

15.

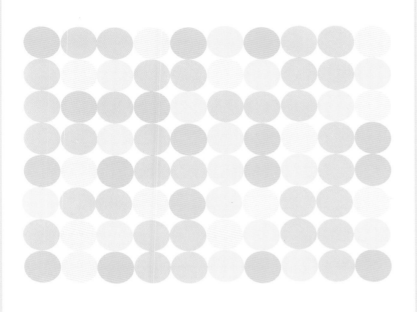

16.

• **Find the blue circles lying horizontally between the green and yellow circles.**

10	17	12	9
A	B	C	D

• **Find the number of squares intersecting orange semicircles.**

11	27	13	21
A	B	C	D

17.

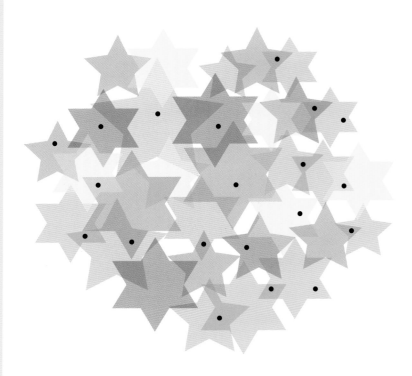

18.

- **Find the number of black dots in the pink stars.**

10	12	9	20
A	B	C	D

- **Find the number of triangles containing a black star.**

19	39	20	22
A	B	C	D

19.

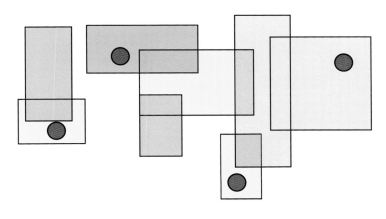

20.

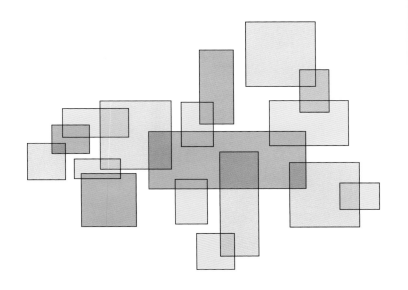

- **Find the number of rectangles which do not contain a red dot.**

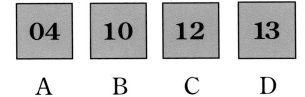

04	10	12	13
A	B	C	D

- **How many squares intersect pink rectangles?**

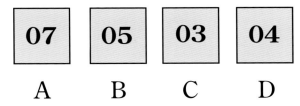

07	05	03	04
A	B	C	D

21.

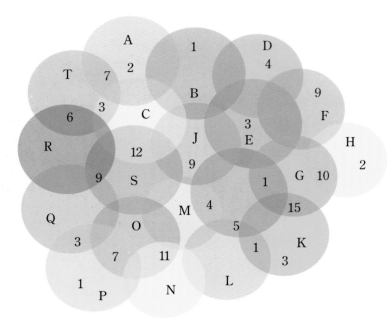

● **Find out which three circles add up to 8.**

BDE	EFG	ABC	EGH
A	B	C	D

22.

● **Find the number of green squares intersecting orange circles.**

11	7	24	8
A	B	C	D

23.

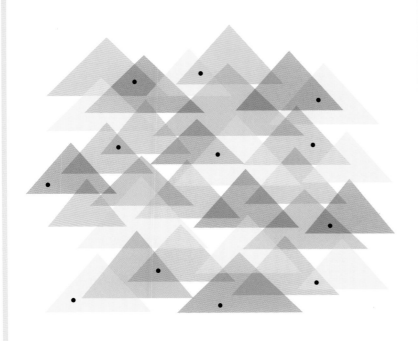

24.

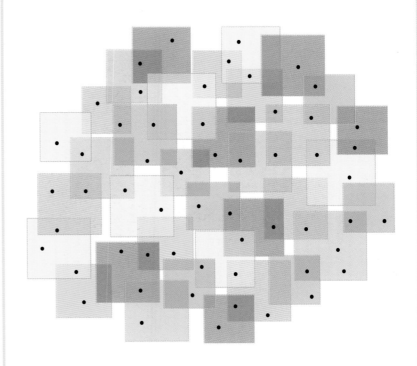

• **How many triangles contain a black dot ?**

10	17	20	28
A	B	C	D

• **Find the number of squares containing more than 2 black dots.**

18	12	14	13
A	B	C	D

25.

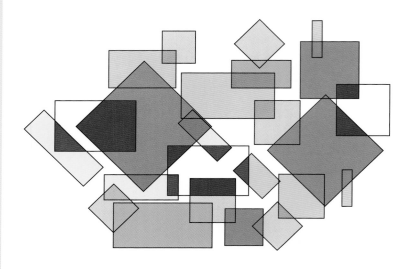

- How many times do the purple squares intersect the pink rectangles?

02	03	04	05
A	B	C	D

26.

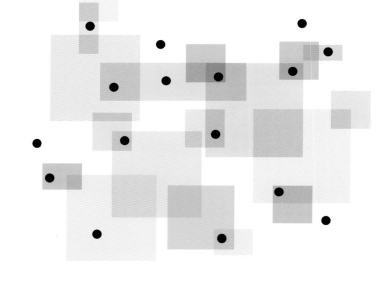

- How many squares contain a black dot?

15	10	11	16
A	B	C	D

WORD FIND

- Each puzzle in this section has specific instructions.
- Read each question carefully before you solve the puzzle.
- Try solving puzzles in the easy and medium category in two minutes, and puzzles in the difficult category in one minute.

1.

Every answer is a 6 letter word that reads from left to right in the row that corresponds to the clue alphabet.

a	P				
b		L			
c			A		
d				Y	
e					E
f						R

a : Pushing or Jabbing
b : Entice
c : Land next to the sea (Plural)
d : Unbleached
e : Mail
f : To make as hard as brass

2.

The names of 9 sports are hidden in the puzzle given below . Try to locate them.

Y	G	O	L	O	N	H	C	E	T	O	I	B	P
P	R	U	G	B	Y	B	S	I	D	T	R	O	H
A	C	S	H	O	R	T	P	U	T	T	O	G	G
R	H	O	R	T	E	C	U	H	T	U	R	N	Y
E	A	C	C	O	H	N	T	A	N	C	I	L	M
H	N	E	U	G	C	A	D	N	D	K	R	I	N
T	E	B	S	N	R	S	U	D	I	A	T	A	A
O	N	Y	T	I	A	K	G	B	E	I	A	I	S
I	A	E	I	S	R	I	N	A	L	M	I	M	T
D	M	E	D	I	C	I	N	L	D	R	H	R	I
R	R	O	D	T	A	N	R	L	A	A	C	A	C
Y	Y	R	U	T	A	G	E	L	D	A	R	T	S
A	A	U	N	E	S	A	M	O	E	N	S	N	Y
N	N	U	E	V	G	L	A	G	D	A	P	A	R
E	O	B	A	D	T	A	R	Y	I	C	A	C	A
M	S	I	L	A	N	C	A	N	O	E	I	N	G

3.

The last names of 3 famous scientists have been jumbled up and merged in this pattern. Unscramble and identify those three scientists.

D	G	T	W	E	E	N
L	N	A	I	O		
N	O	W	A			
R	L					
I						

4.

Unscramble the letter tiles to reveal a proverb.

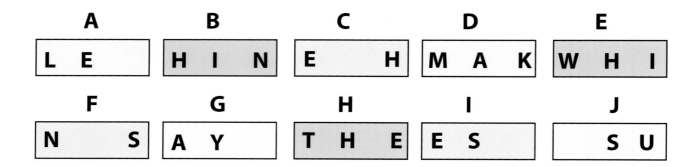

5.

Unscramble the letter tiles to reveal a proverb.

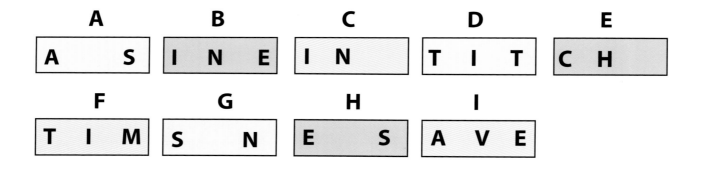

6.

Unscramble the letter tiles to reveal a proverb.

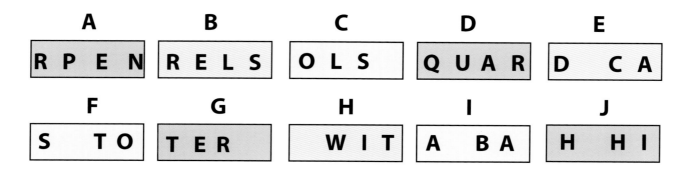

7.

Every answer is a 7 letter word that reads from left to right in the row that corresponds to the clue alphabet.

	1	2	3	4	5	6	7
a	D						
b		R					
c			O				
d				U			
e					G		
f						H	
g							T

a : Temporary state of confusion (Plural)
b : Worn around the arm
c : Life development
d : Ornamental clasp used in Ancient Rome to fasten clothing
e : Promised
f : Physical or mental activity
g : An insect with a shrill sound

8.

Every answer is a 8 letter word that reads from left to right in the row that corresponds to the clue alphabet.

	1	2	3	4	5	6	7	8
a	S							
b		E						
c			M					
d				A				
e					N			
f						T		
g							I	
h								C

a : Small sparkling object
b : Physical fitness program
c : Determined by mathematics or computer
d : Concerned with the interests and welfare of humans
e : Management of land or rural economy
f : A person who performs a task
g : Likeness of a person
h : Skeptical about god

9.

Every answer is a 7 letter word that reads from left to right in the row that corresponds to the clue alphabet.

a	A						
b		D					
c			J				
d				U			
e					R		
f						O	
g							R

a : To sprinkle, especially with holy water
b : The commander in chief of a fleet
c : A royal personage
d : Hormone derived from the pancreas
e : A defensive covering
f : To edge with a series of curved projections
g : A computer output device that draws graphs or pictures, usually by moving a pen

10.

The names of 10 professions are hidden in the puzzle given below. Try to locate them.

Y	G	O	L	O	N	H	C	E	T	O	I	B	P
P	U	E	S	A	O	B	S	I	D	T	R	O	H
A	C	H	G	E	R	O	N	T	O	L	O	G	Y
R	H	O	R	T	I	C	U	L	T	U	R	E	S
E	A	C	C	O	U	N	T	A	N	C	Y	L	I
H	N	E	U	G	A	A	D	R	D	I	R	I	O
T	E	B	S	N	M	E	U	C	N	A	T	A	T
O	N	Y	T	I	E	R	G	H	E	I	A	I	H
I	A	E	I	S	R	A	I	A	L	M	I	M	E
D	M	E	D	I	C	I	N	E	D	R	H	R	R
R	R	O	D	T	C	T	R	O	A	A	C	A	A
Y	Y	R	U	R	A	T	E	L	E	T	Y	T	P
A	A	U	S	E	S	A	M	O	E	N	S	N	Y
N	N	E	E	V	G	L	A	G	D	A	P	A	R
E	E	B	A	D	T	A	R	Y	I	C	A	C	A
M	S	I	L	A	N	R	U	O	J	O	U	R	N

11.

The names of 9 famous international airlines are hidden in the puzzle given below.
Try to locate them.

D	E	L	T	A	A	I	R	L	I	N	E	S	E	S
A	I	R	C	A	D	H	N	A	L	F	D	D	S	S
A	D	P	J	I	J	G	F	B	V	N	V	N	V	M
B	R	T	O	D	N	H	E	J	M	O	E	S	S	N
E	R	A	T	I	S	H	J	K	L	L	L	L	H	V
L	U	I	A	M	E	R	I	A	S	S	I	W	S	C
A	L	I	T	E	L	A	I	F	R	A	N	O	E	I
S	W	I	S	I	T	I	N	O	J	K	O	M	T	F
N	O	T	W	E	S	T	R	I	A	L	I	T	A	I
A	I	I	N	D	I	H	P	A	I	I	N	I	R	C
H	I	O	T	H	J	O	A	I	R	I	N	D	I	A
T	E	U	R	A	S	O	P	I	F	H	F	U	M	P
F	C	S	T	S	O	H	G	L	R	G	K	H	E	Y
U	F	T	H	A	S	A	L	U	A	W	I	I	K	A
L	U	F	T	I	H	D	S	K	N	B	A	V	H	H
L	J	G	I	H	F	G	Y	K	C	L	J	Y	G	T
B	H	B	R	U	T	F	H	K	E	H	J	M	S	A
S	A	I	R	C	A	N	A	D	A	L	L	O	N	C

12.

The names of 10 multinational software companies are hidden in the puzzle given below. Try to locate them.

```
M A C R A A D G G G D H D F B
S I L I C D B L H B O E J K M
U N C A P G E M I N I W M L U
N N M R K N L C B B M L N H J
M O O N O S O G M E T E T H N
I B M L H S G O O G H T M N L
C E L C A R O R I C L T O L P
R P O L P T B F N B J P J L C
O B F J W S S U T B N A K K E
S V N M H I U F E H M C N J E
Y N M M J V H L O H K B G R
S S T Q G J L U H J K A U N U
T M I V R O S O G R J R H N T
E H K H R D E W A V A D M P N
M N L E W A S S R T R F C A E
S B M W O U N S N S E N Z O C
Z E N N L E O P O L U V H J C
G I G E Z B B I N E E L P P A
```

13.

The names of 8 famous car manufacturing companies are hidden in the puzzle given below. Try to locate them.

```
M R C E D A D F H J O L J F V
M E K H J D U H D D H F I F O
D D R Q V U J F S A S A V Y L
G G X C O R O L A F T C E X K
O C T A E V I A V I F C D X S
B M C S S D A W R C H T D S W
S H I C H J E S F C H D F S A
L V I K U Z U S U S U K C B G
L U F F U D T F V I G D T E E
A C Y O H J O F S K O D A W N
H B E N Y O W A G O N C T C C
X G H S W X B Y S D F F O C J
U P F E D C J D D J E U Y Z V
A Q A A C Y C X T W D S O D I
V D K D S V T D C Y S D T I L
```

14.

The names of 8 rivers on the banks of which famous cities are situated are hidden in the puzzle given below. Try to locate them.

```
C D M T B Z B Z U W L A F D J
J I U R W R G Y L A K F O B C
Y K U L I W T Z W C R L A H L
H H M F E L X S V C F B D L N
L M G A L F M D K I P C G R X
H T K P Z O N R B R X B N J R
Z J I Q L V X W W M E Y H O K
T V O D M T J C I O U B U V S
N H A J Z Q O V W S N R I R E
F U A C H Y F W U K D Q Q T L
Q N F M H W I F Z V A O V M I
H W X L E B A O O A N X E D N
X P Z G F S E C N R U Q K W C
M A I N R N B I A E N I E S X
N G F A D B I L T Q I F E I S
```

15.

The names of 8 hollywood divas are hidden in the puzzle given below. Try to locate them.

```
A N G E L I N A J O L I E L Q
A F J G T H K C S C Y B D T V
N L I B T E Y L R O F D C B K
J I J I K L L V D V C B F F V
E Z C C J C C S H D J D D G G
N T G O U F S F N F C C M R C
N A J U L C D F F I L J Y E D
I Y H K I E F E T R W F H T O
F L L I A K K I D W C E F A K
E O R O R V B I F J L L T G E
R R O B O G A R D O G T E A R
L D D H B M H E W M W V K R K
O A N G E R A G R E A T F B J
P O M A R I L Y N M O N R O E
E T R W T I O V A Q Q F V H I
Z P O G S D R V H H T G R E T
```

16.

The names of 8 football playing nations are hidden in the puzzle given below. Try to locate them.

L	I	S	B	D	F	G	H	D	E	N	B	A
A	R	G	A	T	N	A	N	A	F	C	J	F
G	G	A	F	R	S	A	V	J	T	S	C	C
U	P	O	R	G	L	A	G	K	L	V	D	G
T	K	G	A	G	R	D	X	B	X	R	I	E
R	A	N	N	V	E	A	A	Y	I	T	L	R
O	F	E	C	G	L	N	I	K	G	B	V	M
P	L	P	E	B	C	S	T	R	A	R	K	A
R	C	N	R	F	C	R	A	I	G	Z	G	N
P	O	R	U	H	D	T	L	A	N	I	Q	Y
D	H	J	F	L	L	H	Y	S	P	A	I	N
S	P	A	N	I	A	L	D	A	N	L	E	C
D	E	R	Z	I	Y	L	F	F	F	T	E	N
A	A	A	I	Y	T	D	D	G	I	X	F	V
R	R	S	T	R	U	J	L	D	V	N	H	D
B	B	F	H	Y	I	H	F	E	F	O	F	D

18.

The names of 12 cities are hidden in the puzzle given below. Try to locate them.

A	T	E	L	B	W	O	C	S	O	M
U	E	S	E	D	I	S	O	D	F	I
C	H	I	N	A	T	Y	N	N	R	N
E	R	R	B	P	K	R	A	S	A	D
R	L	M	N	O	L	N	E	E	N	I
N	U	O	T	N	O	R	O	T	K	A
M	U	M	B	E	T	E	R	T	F	O
S	Y	R	P	A	R	I	S	O	U	B
S	L	E	L	I	O	I	N	N	R	M
H	A	P	A	N	M	S	C	D	T	O
A	T	D	G	D	E	Y	E	A	T	L
N	I	U	N	I	T	D	N	E	W	O
G	L	O	N	D	O	N	E	E	L	C
H	E	E	N	G	L	E	N	D	A	D
A	B	D	Y	L	T	Y	L	L	T	E
I	D	N	A	K	R	O	Y	W	E	N

17.

The names of 8 sports people are hidden in the puzzle given below. Try to locate them.

A	N	N	A	K	O	U	R	N	I	K	O	V	A
U	N	S	E	D	B	S	D	D	B	S	D	B	R
R	E	D	G	N	T	Y	N	N	T	Y	N	T	Z
O	R	U	R	E	E	R	N	E	E	R	E	E	H
N	L	N	O	E	L	E	E	E	L	E	E	L	S
A	E	E	G	D	A	D	D	D	A	T	D	A	B
L	A	D	E	L	Z	G	L	L	A	E	D	T	J
D	N	R	R	E	R	G	A	M	O	G	E	O	W
I	D	E	F	B	I	T	P	S	A	T	D	A	U
N	E	S	E	D	M	R	D	D	S	L	D	B	P
H	R	D	D	N	A	Y	G	N	A	I	N	T	K
O	P	U	E	S	I	R	N	N	E	R	E	E	T
R	A	N	R	E	N	E	O	E	L	E	E	L	H
N	E	E	D	A	R	D	D	A	D	D	A	Y	
E	S	D	R	L	S	E	L	L	T	E	L	T	E
S	A	R	P	M	A	S	E	T	E	P	E	O	G

19.

Every answer is a 7 letter word that reads from left to right in the row that corresponds to the clue alphabet.

	1	2	3	4	5	6	7
a	J						
b		A					
c			C				
d				K			
e					P		
f						O	
g							T

a : To vindicate
b : Directed to the side
c : Embrace
d : Hammer with flattened edge to dig
e : Member of a theatrical company
f : A gaseous suspension of fine solid or liquid particles
g : Spirally curled lock of hair

20.

Every answer is a 6 letter word that reads from left to right in the row that corresponds to the clue alphabet.

	1	2	3	4	5	6
a	D					
b		E				
c			F			
d				I		
e					N	
f						E

a : To strike or hit lightly
b : Situation of noisy uproar and confusion.
c : Twofold
d : To support
e : Dignity of a baron
f : To cower

21.

Every answer is a 6 letter word that reads from left to right in the row that corresponds to the clue alphabet.

	1	2	3	4	5	6
a	F					
b		L				
c			U			
d				M		
e					E	
f						S

a : To rot or decay
b : Stare angrily
c : Trinket
d : To beat using fists
e : Dry red wine made in Bordeaux
f : Distinguishing features

22.

Every answer is a 6 letter word that reads from left to right in the row that corresponds to the clue alphabet.

	1	2	3	4	5	6
a	P					
b		E				
c			L			
d				T		
e					E	
f						R

a : Preceding the main event
b : Pungent spice
c : Young ones of an owl
d : A piece of literature written in verse
e : To honour or award
f : Drink of the gods

23.

The names of 9 Olympic games' venues are hidden in the puzzle given below.
Try to locate them.

Y	G	H	L	O	N	H	C	E	T	Y
L	L	E	A	T	H	E	N	S	S	T
O	O	L	H	O	R	T	P	U	T	I
N	N	S	R	T	E	C	U	H	O	C
E	D	I	A	O	H	N	T	A	C	O
H	O	N	U	N	C	A	D	N	K	C
T	N	K	S	N	G	S	U	D	H	I
O	N	I	T	I	A	E	G	B	O	X
I	A	E	I	S	R	I	L	A	L	E
M	E	L	B	O	U	R	N	E	M	M
R	R	O	D	T	P	A	R	I	S	A
Y	B	A	R	C	E	L	O	N	A	A
A	A	U	N	E	S	A	M	O	E	N

24.

The names of 7 Shire countries in England are hidden in the puzzle given below.
Try to locate them.

B	P	H	F	X	V	E	S	A	Z	U	N	K	F	S
D	E	R	R	T	M	S	B	I	V	B	X	C	G	I
H	M	M	A	P	I	O	C	S	C	D	D	C	B	E
L	F	A	Q	W	S	Y	K	H	I	N	Y	C	W	M
N	E	T	I	C	S	Y	I	K	H	D	U	L	X	E
A	L	C	A	L	R	E	O	F	E	L	A	X	X	N
S	T	E	G	N	Y	R	A	S	S	N	D	U	L	S
O	C	E	N	O	K	I	S	O	M	W	T	R	N	I
N	C	C	U	K	G	E	C	M	O	X	K	T	S	R
S	U	S	S	E	X	S	S	E	L	P	Q	Y	E	K
C	O	U	R	S	G	S	A	R	S	E	R	N	D	L
E	N	F	S	A	C	O	U	S	U	R	R	E	Y	O
W	I	L	T	S	H	I	R	E	Q	R	R	D	V	F
Y	S	T	W	C	K	K	Q	T	R	H	U	R	L	R
Y	X	O	D	J	V	Y	B	B	K	R	O	T	O	O
C	N	M	S	F	V	J	N	D	G	G	B	Y	R	N

Reposition

- **In the given puzzles the positions of two symbols have been interchanged once.**
- **Reposition them in their original place So that the puzzle would follow a proper sequence.**
- **The legend will provide you with the sequence.**
- **Remember the sequence can start from any point.**

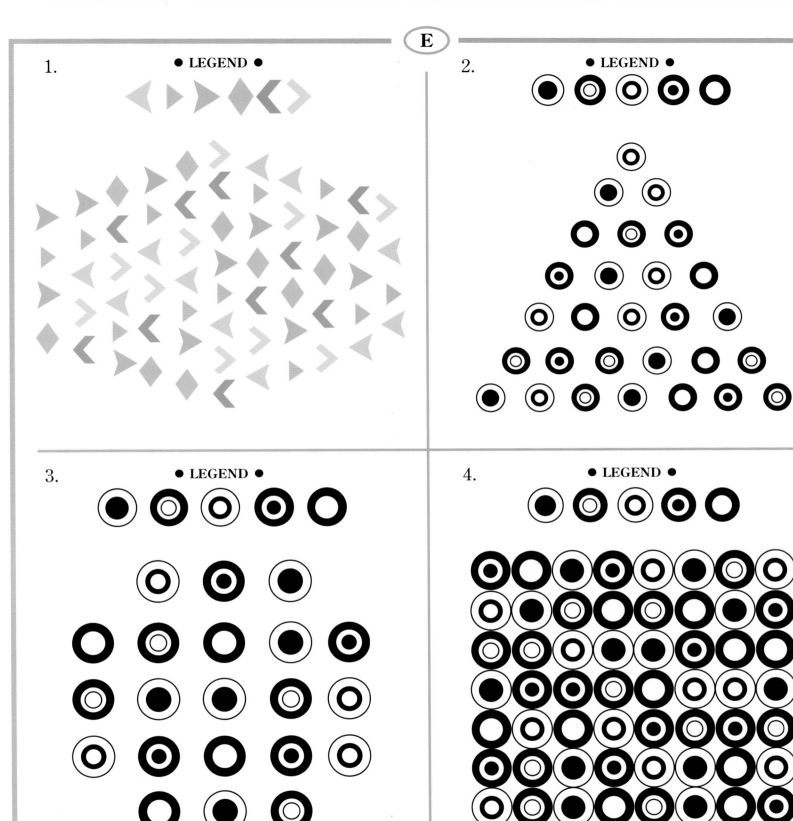

195

5.

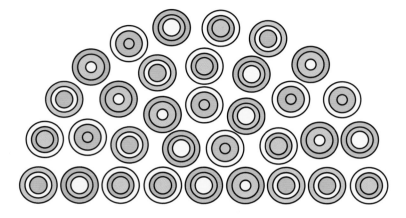

6.

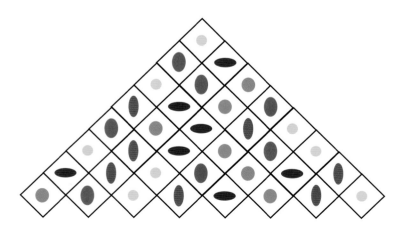

7. ● LEGEND ●

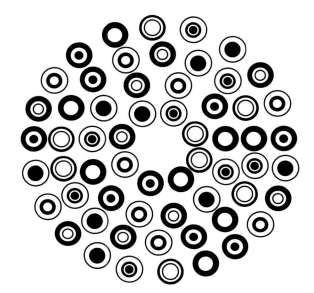

8. ● LEGEND ●

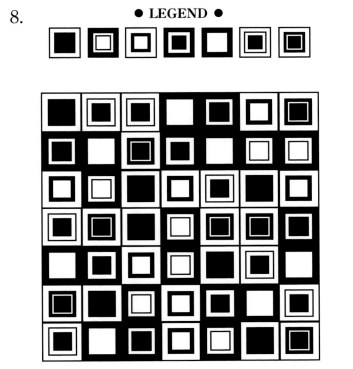

9. ● LEGEND ●

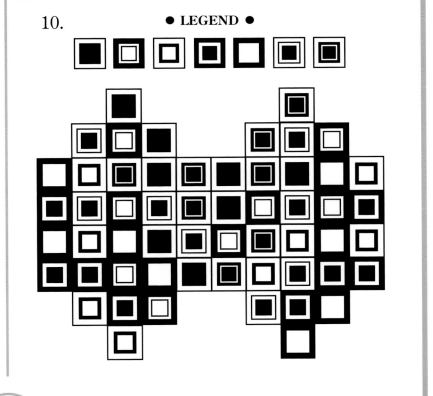

10. ● LEGEND ●

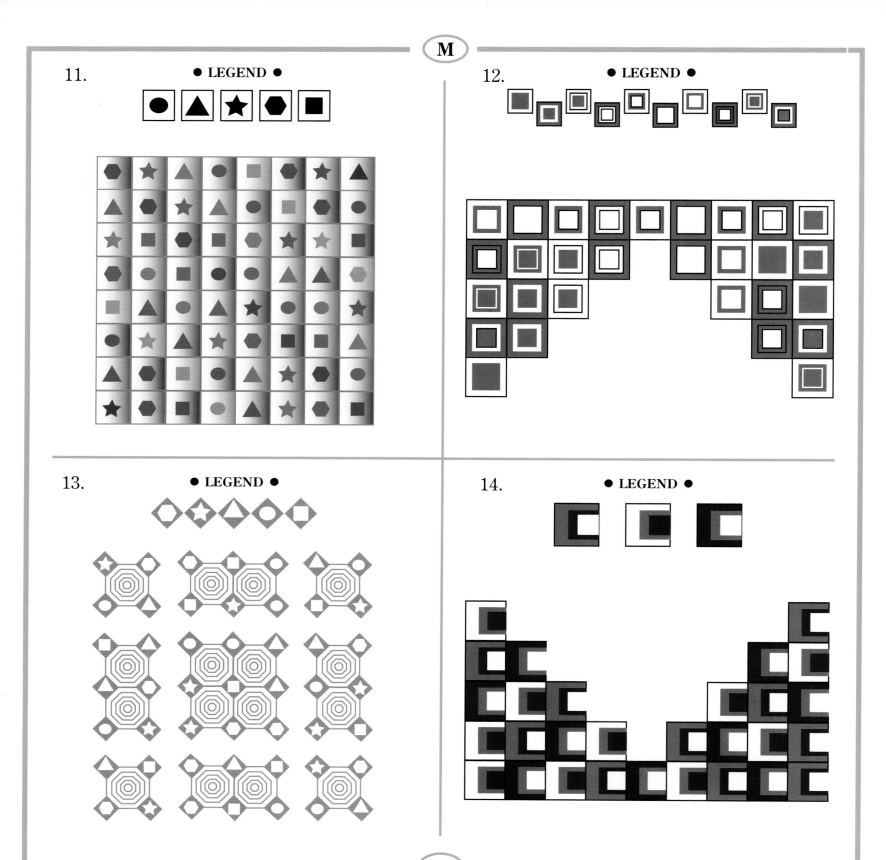

15.

16.

17.

18.

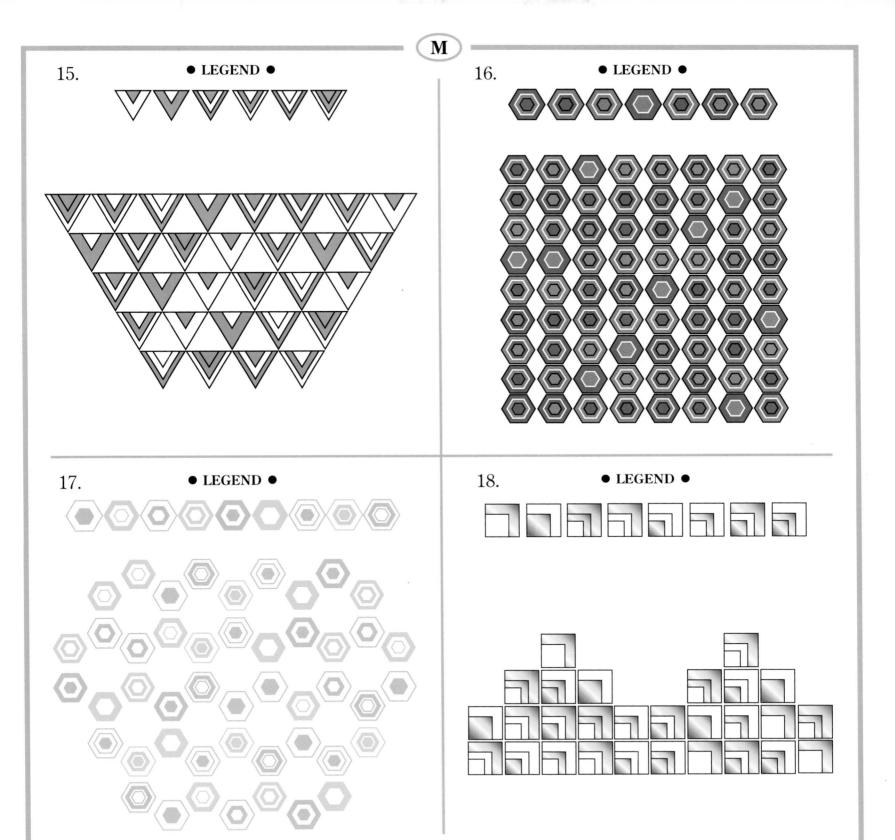

19.

20.

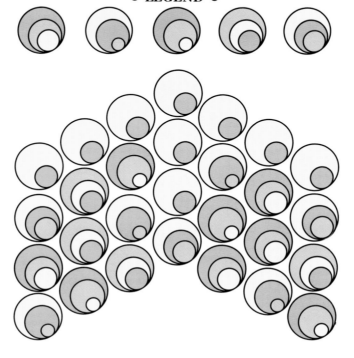

21.

● LEGEND ●

22.

● LEGEND ●

23.

● LEGEND ●

24.

● LEGEND ●

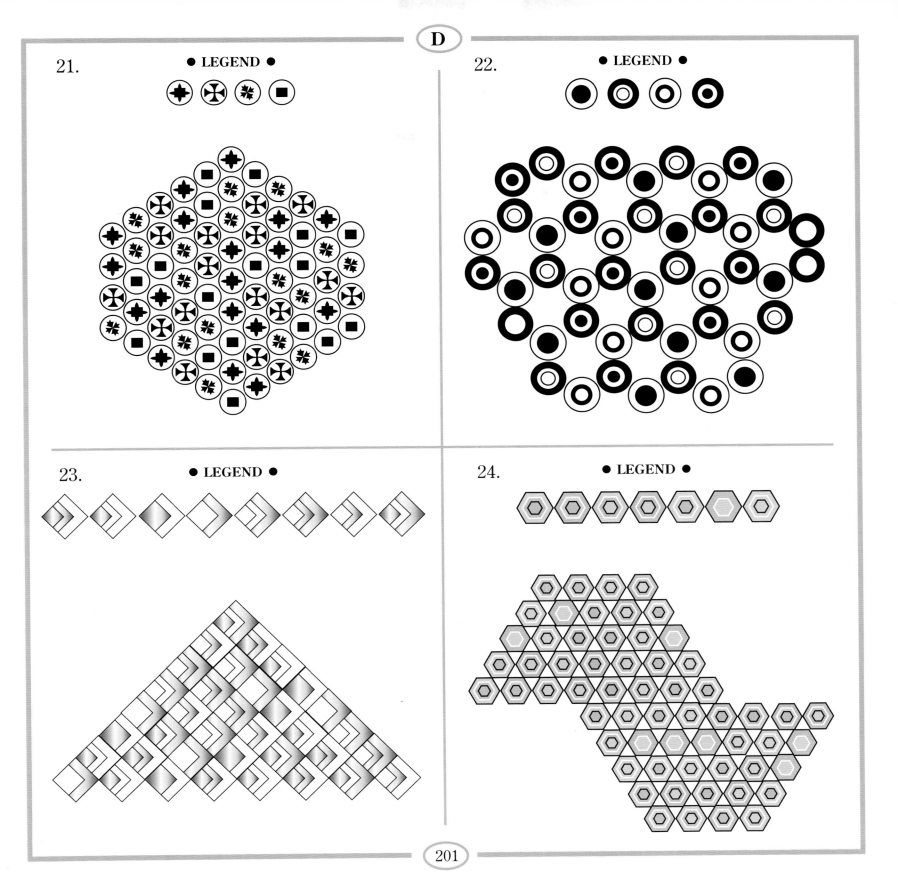

25.

26.

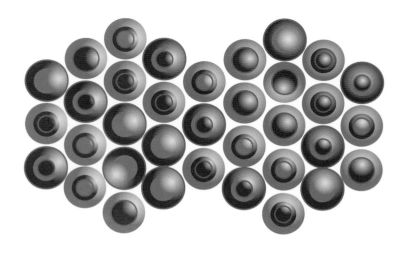

PERFECT CUT

- In the series of puzzles that follow, instructions would differ from puzzle to puzzle.
- Read each question carefully before you solve the puzzle.

1.

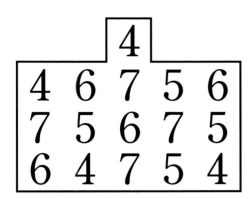

- Divide the diagram into four parts of equal size and shape.
- Each part must contain the numbers 4, 5, 6 and 7.
- The four parts should then be rearranged to form a square.

2.

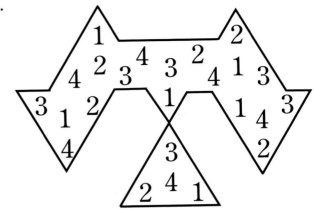

- Divide the diagram into six parts of equal size and shape.
- Each part must contain the numbers 1, 2, 3 and 4.
- The six parts should then be rearranged to form a hexagon.

3.

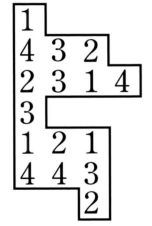

- Divide the diagram into four parts of equal size and shape.
- Each part must contain the numbers 1, 2, 3 and 4.
- The four parts should then be rearranged to form a square.

4.

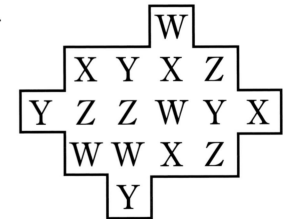

- Divide the diagram into four parts of equal size and shape.
- Each part must contain the letters W, X, Y and Z.
- The four parts should then be rearranged to form a square.

5.

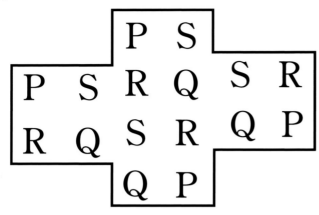

- Divide the diagram into four parts of equal size and shape.
- Each part must contain the letters P, Q, R and S.
- The four parts should then be rearranged to form a square.

6.

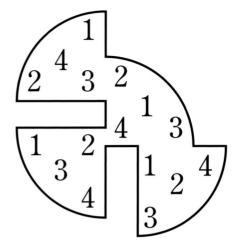

- Divide the diagram into four parts of equal size and shape.
- Each part must contain the numbers 1, 2, 3 and 4.
- The four parts should then be rearranged to form a circle.

7.

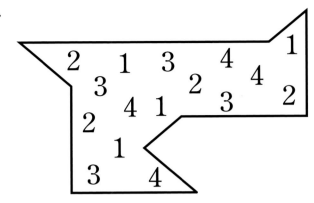

- Divide the diagram into four parts of equal size and shape.
- Each part must contain the numbers 1, 2, 3 and 4.
- The four parts should then be rearranged to form a rectangle.

8.

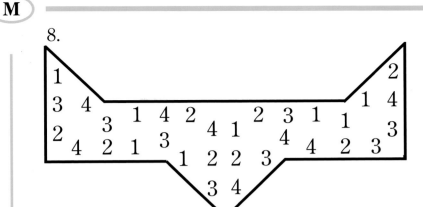

- Divide the diagram into eight parts of equal size and shape.
- Each part must contain the numbers 1, 2, 3 and 4.
- The eight parts should then be rearranged to form a rectangle.

9.

- Divide the diagram into four parts of equal size and shape.
- Each part must contain the numbers 1, 2, 3 and 4.
- The four parts should then be rearranged to form a rectangle.

10.

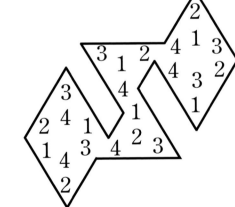

- Divide the diagram into six parts of equal size and shape.
- Each part must contain the numbers 1, 2, 3 and 4.
- The six parts should then be rearranged to form a hexagon.

11.

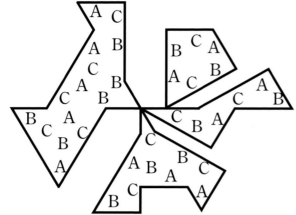

- Divide the diagram into twelve parts of equal size and shape.
- Each part must contain the letters A, B and C.
- The twelve parts should then be rearranged to form a hexagon.

12.

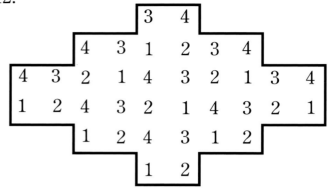

- Divide the diagram into nine parts of equal size and shape.
- Each part must contain the numbers 1, 2, 3 and 4.
- The nine parts should then be rearranged to form a square.

13.

```
      D C
      A B
      C D B A
      B A C D
B D B A D C A B C D
C A C D A B D C B A
      B A
      C D
```

- Divide the diagram into nine parts of equal size and shape.
- Each part must contain the letters A, B, C and D.
- The nine parts should then be rearranged to form a square.

14.

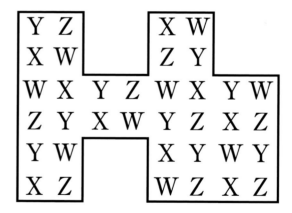

- Divide the diagram into nine parts of equal size and shape.
- Each part must contain the letters W, X, Y and Z.
- The nine parts should then be rearranged to form a square.

15.

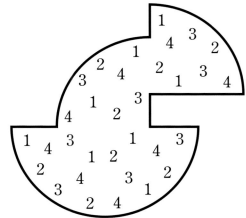

- Divide the diagram into eight parts of equal size and shape.
- Each part must contain the numbers 1, 2, 3 and 4.
- The eight parts should then be rearranged to form a circle.

16.

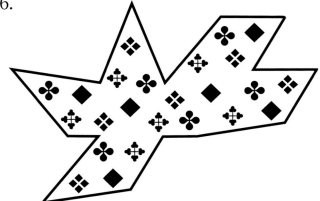

- Divide the diagram into six parts of equal size and shape.
- Each part must contain the symbols ♣, ❖, ◆ and ✛.
- The six parts should then be rearranged to form a star.

17.

- Divide the diagram into six parts of equal size and shape.
- Each part must contain the symbols ♣, ❖, ◆ and ✛.
- The six parts should then be rearranged to form a star.

18.

- Divide the diagram into six parts of equal size and shape.
- Each part must contain the symbols ★, ✧, ☆ and ✭.
- The six parts should then be rearranged to form a star.

19.

- Divide the diagram into six parts of equal size and shape.
- Each part must contain the symbols ✷ , ✧ , ✩ and ✦.
- The six parts should then be rearranged to form a star.

20.

- Divide the diagram into six parts of equal size and shape.
- Each part must contain the symbols ✷ , ✧ , ✩ and ✦.
- The six parts should then be rearranged to form a star.

21.

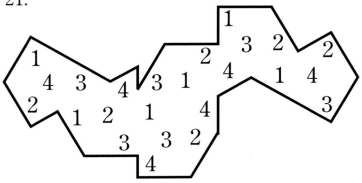

- Divide the diagram into six parts of equal size and shape.
- Each part must contain the numbers 1, 2, 3 and 4.
- The six parts should then be rearranged to form a hexagon.

22.

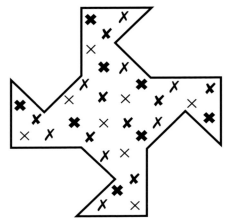

- Divide the diagram into eight parts of equal size and shape.
- Each part must contain the symbols ×, ✗, ✘ and ✖.
- The eight parts should then be rearranged to form a square.

23.

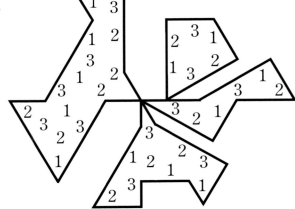

- Divide the diagram into twelve parts of equal size and shape.
- Each part must contain the numbers 1, 2, and 3.
- The twelve parts should then be rearranged to form a hexagon.

24.

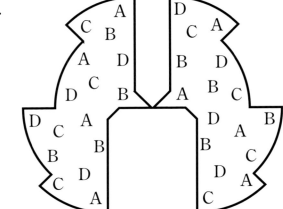

- Divide the diagram into eight parts of equal size and shape.
- Each part must contain the letters A, B, C and D.
- The eight parts should then be rearranged to form a circle.

25.

- Divide the diagram into eight parts of equal size and shape.
- Each part must contain the letters A, B, C and D.
- The eight parts should then be rearranged to form a square.

26.

- Divide the diagram into eight parts of equal size and shape.
- Each part must contain the symbols ✕, ✗, ✘ and ✖.
- The eight parts should then be rearranged to form a square.

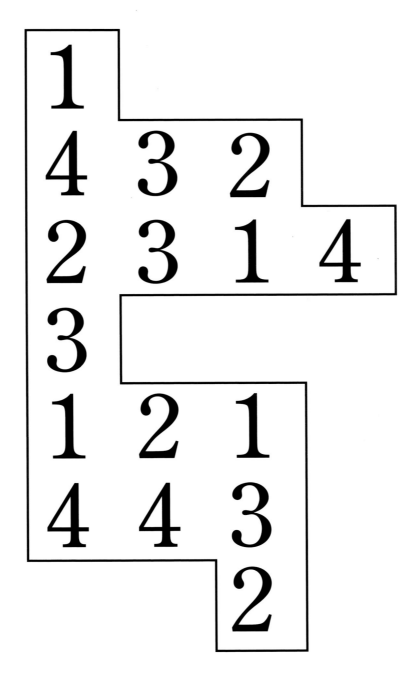

Sudoku

- For the puzzles with four or six boxes, fill each square with a color (from the legend) in such a way that every color appears only once in each horizontal row and vertical column.

- For the puzzles with 9 boxes & color legend given, fill each square with a color (from the legend) in such a way that every color appears only once in each of the nine boxes, as well as once in each horizontal row & vertical column.

- For the puzzles with 9 boxes & symbol legend given, fill each square with a symbol (from the legend) in such a way that every symbol appears only once in each of the nine boxes, as well as once in each horizontal row and vertical column.

1. ● LEGEND -

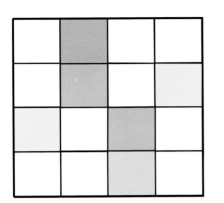

2. ● LEGEND -

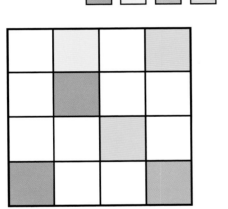

3. ● LEGEND -

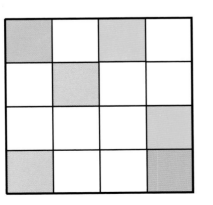

4. ● LEGEND -

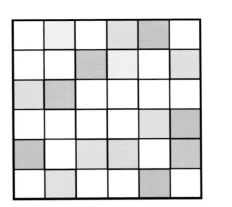

5. ● LEGEND -

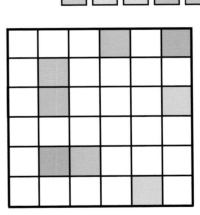

6. ● LEGEND -

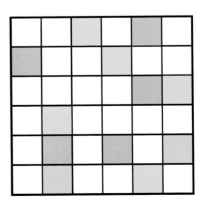

● LEGEND -

7.

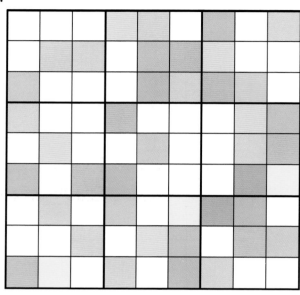

9.

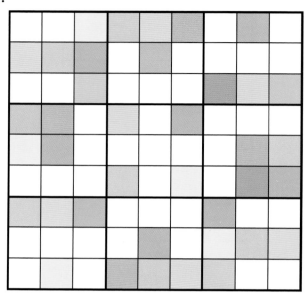

8.

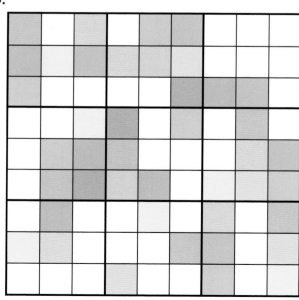

10.

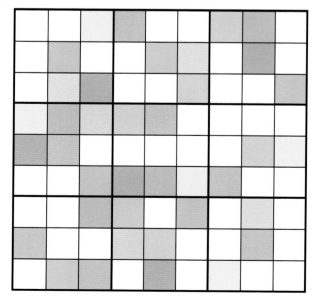

● LEGEND - △ □ ○ Ω ✕ ◇ + √ ☆

11.

		□	√			◇	△	
	☆			Ω	○		✕	
	○	✕			◇			☆
□	△	+	◇	√				
✕	√						◇	□
		☆	✕	△	□	√		
		△	Ω		√		○	
☆			+	◇			√	
	Ω	√		✕		□		

13.

			□					○
○	✕					△		□
	☆			○		✕		Ω
	Ω	+	◇	☆		○	□	
	√	☆	Ω				✕	△
		○	+		√		Ω	
√					+	☆	△	
☆			✕	◇	□			
Ω		✕		√	△			

12.

		✕	□	◇	+			
☆				✕		◇	□	○
	□	Ω					✕	△
○			√		✕	□	◇	
			○		☆			
	△	√	◇		□			+
+	✕					√	○	
√	Ω	◇			○	✕		
				√	△	Ω	+	

14.

	+			✕	◇			√
	✕	√			◇			○
Ω	○	◇		△				+
	△	Ω			☆			◇
	√			◇	✕			Ω
+	◇	☆			Ω	✕		□
	Ω	✕						☆
	□			☆	√			△
	☆	○			△			✕

● LEGEND - △ □ O Ω ✕ ◇ + √ ☆

15.

☆				✕		△		
Ω	O	□				√		◇
✕			□	◇	O	Ω		
	✕		O		Ω		□	
	△		◇		✕		√	
	☆		△		□		◇	
		√	✕	□	◇			☆
O		✕				◇	△	√
		☆		O				✕

16.

☆	◇	Ω	✕		+			△
	✕			Ω				☆
			O		△			✕
	Ω	◇		□	☆		✕	+
□						√		◇
✕	△		√	◇	O	☆		
			☆					
			◇	O	✕		☆	
△	□	☆	Ω			✕	◇	O

17.

+	☆	△			√	Ω		
√	◇				Ω		□	
				+	△	✕	√	
				◇	✕	+		△
	△	Ω				□		O
☆		+	△	□				
	Ω	◇	O	☆				
	+		√				◇	✕
		□	✕			☆	+	Ω

18.

✕	√	☆	◇	+	Ω			□
△				√		Ω	☆	+
	+		□					√
	△	Ω	☆		✕	+		
						◇		☆
◇	☆		△		+			Ω
√		△	+					✕
	□		√	☆	△		Ω	
☆		◇			□			△

● LEGEND - △ □ ○ Ω × ◇ + √ ☆

19.

Ω						☆	◇	
□			Ω	△	+			
√	△	○		×				+
			□		◇	△	○	
×	◇	Ω					√	☆
	○	□	☆		×			
☆				○		◇	+	√
			+	◇	△			□
	×	+						Ω

21.

	√		○	Ω		△		☆
	△		□				Ω	
Ω	◇		△					○
			×		+			△
	○	□				Ω		×
△	×	◇	√		Ω			
		○		√				□
	+	√		△	□			◇
		△			○	√		Ω

20.

+	□	○	√	△	Ω	×		
							□	Ω
○	◇	□			√			△
	Ω	√				◇	○	
×	+			○	☆		√	
							+	○
		◇	○	×	+	□	Ω	☆

22.

△	◇	√						Ω
	+					√	◇	
			◇	△	√			
	√						×	□
		△			☆			
		◇		□			○	
√	Ω	+						
	△						√	◇
◇					Ω	□	☆	

● LEGEND - △ □ O Ω × ◇ + √ ☆

23.

O				×		◇	+	Ω
◇				△				□
+	☆			◇	Ω			
Ω			×	+	◇	√	O	△
×		O					◇	
		◇	☆	Ω	O			
			Ω	O	△	+	□	
□								
△	O	×					Ω	◇

24.

×						□		
	+		□	△	×	O		
	☆	□		√		×		Ω
			√		△	Ω	×	◇
	√	+	×		Ω	☆		
	Ω	×	☆		□			
			O	×	☆			△
□							☆	O
				□				×

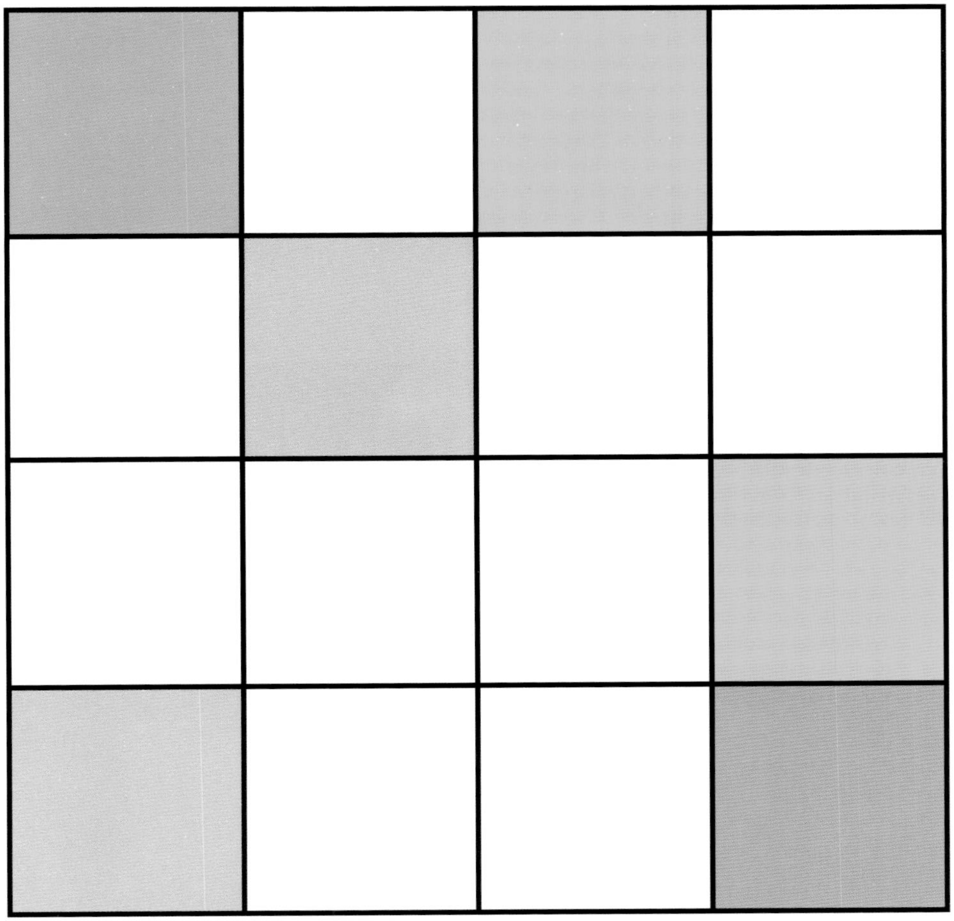

ANSWERS

NUMERICAL

1. A   2. D   3. C   4. D   5. B   6. A   7. B

8. B   9. B   10. C   11. D   12. D   13. B   14. B

15. B   16. C   17. A   18. A

19. B. $2x3 = 6+1 = 7$, $7x3 = 21+1 = 22$, $22x3 = 66+1 = 67$

$4x3 = 12-1 = 11$, $11x3 = 33-1 = 32$, $32x3 = 96-1 = 95$

20. A. $6^2 = 36$, $36+6 = 42$, $9^2 = 81$, $81-9 = 72$

$4^2 = 16$, $16+4 = 20$, $11^2 = 121$, $121-11 = 110$

$8^2 = 64$, $64+8 = 72$, $16^2 = 256$, $256-16 = 240$

$10^2 = 100$, $100+10 = 110$, $12^2 = 144-12 = 132$

21. A. $4^2 = 16$, $16x4 = 64$ & $5^2 = 25$, $25x5 = 125$ &

$7^2 = 49$, $7x49 = 343$ & $9^2 = 81$, $81x9 = 729$ &

$125+64 = 189$, $729-343 = 386$ &

$125-64 = 61$, $729+343 = 1072$

22. B. $2x2 = 4$, $4x2 = 8$, $8x2 = 16$, $16x2 = 32$ &

$32x2 = 64$, $64x2 = 128$, $128x2 = 256$ &

$256+32 = 288$, $288+64 = 352$, $352+128 = 480$,

$480+256 = 736$ & $736+288 = 1024$, $1024+352 = 1376$,

$1376+480 = 1856$, $1856+736 = 2592$

23. B. $4^2 = 16$, $8^3 = 512$, $4+8 = 12$, $12^2 = 144$

$9^2 = 81$, $7^3 = 343$, $7+9 = 16$, $16^2 = 256$

$3^2 = 9$, $6^3 = 216$, $3+6 = 9$, $9^2 = 81$

$5^2 = 25$, $10^3 = 1000$, $10+5 = 15$, $15^2 = 225$

24. D. $6^2 = 36$, $8^2 = 64$, $64-36 = 28$, $28x2 = 56$ &

$15^2 = 225$, $9^2 = 81$, $225-81 = 144$, $144x2 = 288$

$7^2 = 49$, $12^2 = 144$, $144-49 = 95$, $95x2 = 190$

$4^2 = 16$, $11^2 = 121$, $121-16 = 105$, $105x2 = 210$

OBSERVATION

1. S (Missing Letter - O)   2. F (Missing Letter - D)

3. K (Missing Letter - M)   4. Q (Missing Letter - U)

5. S (Missing Letter - P)   6. T (Missing Letter - E)

7. N (Missing Letter - V)   8. V (Missing Letter - N)

9. Y (Missing Letter - B)   10. S (Missing Letter - C)

11. W (Missing Letter - M)   12. M (Missing Letter - I)

13. P (Missing Letter - G)   14. C (Missing Letter - O)

15. U (Missing Letter - Z)   16. O (Missing Letter - H)

17. K (Missing Letter - V)   18. H (Missing Letter - C)

19. F (Missing Letter - N)   20. Q (Missing Letter - q)

21. k (Missing Letter - i)   22. s (Missing Letter - Z)

23. r (Missing Letter - D)   24. G (Missing Letter - T)

ANALOGIES

1. C   2. A   3. B   4. B   5. A   6. D   7. D

8. A   9. C   10. A   11. C   12. D   13. D   14. B

15. B   16. A   17. D   18. C

19. C. If all the parts of the second figure of the problem are joined the first figure of the problem i.e. 'T' is made. In the same way, all the parts of only the answer option 'C' can be joined together to make the problem figure 'F'.

20. A. The first and the second figure of the problem are related to each other, as they are mirror reflections of each other. Also the color that is inside the first figure moves to the outer part of the second figure and vice versa. Both the principles are fulfilled only by answer figure 'A'.

21. B. The second figure of the problem figure is the water reflection of the first figure. Similarly answer 'B' is the water reflection of the third problem figure.

22. B. The color of the 'flower' in figure one becomes the background of figure two and vice versa.

23. D. The second figure will rotate clockwise, identical smaller shapes get added in which colors are added.

24. D. The second shape rotates clockwise, inside color of the first figure moves to the outer part and vice versa.

CATEGORY

1. A   2. D   3. C   4. E   5. D   6. E   7. E

8. E   9. E   10. B   11. D   12. D   13. E   14. D

15. E   16. D   17. E   18. D

19. C. In all the figures except 'C' the figure is the same; only they have been rotated at various angles. 'C' is different as the orange 'beak shape' is pointing downwards in the green diamond.

20. D. All figures except 'D' are the same; all move clockwise. They all have a green and a red arrow. Only figure 'D' has 2 red arrows.

21. D. In the first triangle 12 x 2=24; 24+2=26 the number in the red triangle. All other figures follow the same principle except 'D'. 32 is wrong as the correct answer should have been 17 x 2 + 2 = 34.

22. C. Except C, all other figures if cut on the given black lines would become 3 sided small figures. Figure 'C' if cut would make 4 sided small figures.

23. D. In figure 'A , B, C and E ', the internal shapes are alternately presented, however in 'D' this principle is not applicable.

24. A. All the figures except figure 'A' are cubes. Only 'A' is a square.

MATCH

1. A   2. B   3. C   4. C   5. C   6. D   7. D

8. C   9. D   10. C   11. D   12. A   13. B   14. C

15. B   16. C   17. B   18. C   19. C   20. C

21. D. This is identical as in the other three figures the colors interchange.

22. D. This is identical as in the other three figures the colors interchange.

23. B. This is identical as in the other three figures the colors interchange.

24. A. This is identical as in the other three figures the colors interchange.

25. C. This is identical as in the other three figures the colors interchange.

26. A. This is identical as in the other three figures the colors interchange.

WATER REFLECTION

• Remember that in all the 'water reflection puzzles' the reflection would always be an inverse image of the problem figure as it is a water reflection i.e. an arrow pointing upwards would have an arrow pointing downwards as its water reflection. Do not confuse it with a mirror image!

1. B   2. D   3. D   4. C   5. B   6. A   7. D

8. B   9. B   10. A   11. B   12. C   13. C   14. B

15. A   16. D   17. A   18. D   19. D   20. A   21. C

22. D   23. D   24. C

SEQUENCE

1. B   2. D   3. B   4. C   5. D   6. B   7. B

8. D   9. D   10. D   11. A   12. A   13. A   14. D

15. B   16. B   17. D   18. D

19. A. In the second problem figure two same direction green lines flip, in the third figure three same direction pink lines flip, in the fourth figure the bottom green line flips. In the next figure only two same color and direction lines should flip.

20. C. Each figure adds orange line segments to the circle alternating between one and two lines.

21. C. In every figure the two colors between the two black squares interchange their positions starting from the largest black square and moving inwards.

22. A. In every figure four inner red lines get subtracted from the hexagons above and three blue lines get added to the rectangles below.

23. D. The dark blue portion and the black dots move in a clockwise direction.

24. B. The square moves clockwise, the colors of the top squares are alternately red and green; the colors inside the circle interchange.

SERIES

1. D   2. A   3. B   4. A   5. B   6. C   7. A

8. A   9. B   10. D   11. D   12. C   13. A   14. B

15. C   16. A   17. D   18. B

19. C. In each row, the common symbols between the first and the second figure stay in the third figure whereas the uncommon symbols are dropped. For instance in the first row the bigger green circle and four lines which are common to both first and second figure stay in the third figure. But the smaller circle present in the first figure and the black dot and extra 4 lines in the second figure are dropped in the third figure.

20. C. In the second and third block of the first row we see that first the white square and 4 lines then the green square rotates clockwise.

21. D. The geometric shape is rotating from the first figure to the second to the third in each row. Also the colors are alternating from one figure to other in such a way that each part of the shape is a different color each time.

22. B. In the first row, the outermost shape; square moves to become the innermost shape in the second figure. The outermost shape in the second figure; circle moves to become the middle figure in the third figure. Same principle applies to the second and third rows.

23. C. In the first row, colors move from the outermost 'right-angle' shape to the innermost shape. Also the two figures are a mirror image of each other.

24. D. In the first row, in the first figure there is a gap of five letters and in the second figure the gap is of three letters.

PATTERN

1. D   2. D   3. C   4. C   5. A   6. D   7. D

8. B   9. B   10. D   11. C   12. D   13. A   14. B

15. D   16. B   17. D   18. C   19. A   20. A

21. C. Answer figures A, B and D cannot be the answer as either the shapes or the colors or both the shapes and colors are changing.

22. C. Answer figures A, B and D cannot be the answer as either the colors or the shapes or both the shapes and colors are changing.

23. D. Answer figures A, B and C cannot be the answer as colors are changing.

24. A. Answer figures B, C and D cannot be the answer as shapes are changing.

25. B. Answer figures A, C and D cannot be the answer as some shapes are missing.

26. C. Answer figures A, B and D cannot be the answer as some shapes are missing.

SIMILARITY

1. B 2. A 3. C 4. D 5. A 6. D 7. A

8. D 9. C 10. D 11. B 12. E 13. A 14. D

15. A 16. B 17. D 18. C

19. F. The tips of only figures 3, 5, and 7 are similarly rounded.

20. B. Figures 1, 5 and 9 contain 2 shapes with four sides. Within the figure, between the two shapes, the colors and the placement of the horizontal lines interchange.

21. D. Only figures 1 and 5 have the same 5 shapes and same 5 colors.

22. A. Only in figures 1 and 6 the black line touches the centre of the figure. Also the red circle touches one of the corners of the purple shape.

23. E. Only figures 1, 6 and 8 contain equal number of triangles [5] with the same colors and equal number of small [4] and big [5] blue dots.

24. F. Only in figures 2, 6 and 7; the 2 similar shapes- the star and the black dot are inside the main shape. Also the impinged pink, black, lavender and blue circles are similar.

BRICKS

1. C 2. D 3. B 4. D 5. C 6. A 7. C

8. A 9. B 10. A 11. A 12. C 13. D 14. A

15. C 16. B 17. D 18. B 19. D 20. D

21. C. In option A, there are 7 yellow triangles instead of 9 yellow triangles, in B a triangle formed by 3 pink triangles is missing, in D, 4 orange triangles interchange with blue triangles.

22. B. In option A there are 8 yellow triangles instead of 7, similarly in option C there are 13 white circles instead of 12 and in option D, there are 11 black circles instead of 10.

23. D. In option A, the center of the figure is incorrect; in option B the small black and white triangles in the larger yellow triangles have interchanged, in C, there are 24 black triangles instead of 20.

24. B. In option A there are only 12 black dots instead of 14; in option C 30 black triangles instead of 26 and in option D there are 24 white dots instead of 20.

25. D. In option A, there are 16 small orange triangles instead of 12; in option B there are 12 black triangles instead of 8, in option C, there are 2 small black and 2 small white dots instead of 4 small white dots.

26. C. In option A, one green square is missing; in option B, white circle is missing in the bottom green square and 28 black triangles instead of 20 and in D, there are 16 black triangles instead of 20.

COLOR PERCEPTION

1. B 2. B 3. B 4. C 5. B 6. C 7. B

8. A 9. D 10. D 11. A 12. B 13. C 14. C

15. D 16. D 17. A 18. B 19. D 20. C

21. A. as in options B, C and D the colors have changed.

22. D. In option A, orange color gets interchanged with pink, in B cream color is missing between yellow and orange similarly in C the pink and violet get interchanged.

23. B. In option A color is changing, in option C white oval shape has rotated and in option D there is a gap between the white circle and spiral shape.

24. B. Colors are changing in options A, C and D.

25. A. In option B a small circle touches the oval shape, in option C the color of top right strip changes and in option D the color of hexagon has changed.

26. C. Shapes and colors are interchanging.

MATRIX

1. A   2. C   3. C   4. C   5. B   6. C   7. B

8. C   9. A   10. C   11. D   12. A   13. B   14. D

15. A   16. A   17. A   18. C   19. C   20. C

21. A. The colors in other 3 options are changing.

22. A. The left and right horizontal lines and the shapes are changing.

23. A. Colors and dots vary in the other 3 options.

24. C. Colors vary in the other 3 options.

25. C. Colors vary in the other 3 options.

26. A. Colors vary in the other 3 options.

WORD POWER

1. Ten, Age, Van, Zen, Vex, Axe, Rat, Rag, Tar, Ear, Ant, Get, Net, Tag, Tear, Rent, Grant, Extra, Gaze, Next, Near, Neat, Vent, Gate, Raze, Rage, Raga, Gran, Rave, Gear, Rant, Rate, Graze, Grave, Agent, Great, Ravage, Vagrant, Extravaganza

2. Belt, Lost, Rest, Toil, Soil, Bust, Best, Rise, Sure, List, Boil, Tube, Site, Crib, Blue, Isle, Lure, Cist, Curl, Silt, Loss, Cure, Soul, Coil, Tire, Sire, Coir, Boss, Toss, Clue, Slit, Bite, Bore, Robe, Rile, Tile, Bile, Bolt, Cult, Lust, Club, Crest, Loser, Rouse, Sober, Cross, Brute, Route, Locus, Tousle, Sister, Bruise, Cluster, Trouble, Tuberculosis

3. Tent, Gate, Tire, Tilt, Gait, Rain, Tart, Cart, Cent, Teal, Tear, Mint, Mate, Meal, Gail, Tail, Rail, Mail, Nail, Tile, Nice, Neat, Trim, Near, Name, Item, Iron, Tame, Grant, More, Roam, Time, Game, Ogre, Tone, Gear, Melt, Mart, Meet, Tram, Meat, Mega, Tonic, Image, Alter, Clear, Elect, Groin, Loner, Meter, Melee, Clean, Great, Micron, Metric, Orient, Cement, Entice, Magnet, Remote, Normal, Electra, Termite, Romance, Romantic, Electromagnetic

4. Line, Lone, Open, Nail, Pole, Load, Peal, Loan, Ploy, Code, Pine, Pain, Plan, Pale, Yelp, Dean, Clap, Deal, Pile, Clip, Eden, Pail, Dial, Lion, Clan, Node, Cope, Peel, Cane, Lend, Pane, Dope, Deep, Lead, Need, Dine, Pond, Plead, Clean, Cycle, Clone, Deploy, Cyclone, Encyclopedia.

5. Oil, Log, Hog, Sip, Lip, Hip, Shy, Sly, Ply, Sop, Hop, Soil, Poly, Loop, Pool, Solo, Polo, Holy, Ploy, Slip, Slog, lisp,

6. Dirt, Tire, Mire, Mane, Maid, Raid, Tame, Tram, Mart, Rant, Rate, Trim, Mast, Meat, Read, Tear, East, Mist, Mind, Team, Ream, Term, Star, Rind, Mare, Ride, Main, Tired, Staid, Dream, Smart, Tread, Stare, Merit, Steam, Retina, Master, Stream, Stride, Retain, Detain, Strand, Mister, Remind, Instead, Mastermind

7. Test, Till, Tale, Slit, Teal, Last, Silt, Seat, Tell, Site, List, Tilt, Lilt, Lest, Tile, Late, Tall, Salt, Tail, Steel, Steal, Elite, Tease, Latest, Least, Still, Stall, Stale, Stilt, Slate, Satellite

8. Mace, Mead, Mode, Dome, Ream, Roam, Dame, Mare, More, Cram, Rome, Come, Cream, Dream, Cameo, Mayor, Mercy, Comedy, Democracy

9. Cat, Can, Cot, Con, Act, Car, Coin, Cart, Corn, Icon, Coir, Carat, Carton, Raincoat

10. Slob, Flub, Also, Slab, Soul, Foul, Fabulous

11. Tic, Tie, Toy, Cot, Yet, Sit, Set, Toe, Site, Cite, Cist, Cost, Sect, City, Society

12. Cart, Tire, Rice, Tart, Rate, Hare, Hire, Rite, Rare, Tear, Sire, Rich, Arch, Rash, Hear, Race, Care, Rest, Hair, Iris, Star, Rise, Stir, Char, Crate, Trace, Trite, Heart, Reach, Trice, Treat, Shirt, Trash, Crash, Chair, Crest, Earth, Retch, Tiara, Arise, Carat, Racer, React, Recast, Crater, Critic, Arctic, Attire, Thirst, Racist, Rather, Sitter, Search, Thrice, Starch, Tartar, Stretch, Archaic, Scratch, Character, Characteristic

13. Sane, Earn, Rent, Tent, Vine, Rein, Vest, Near, Lean, Nail, Line, Neat, Nest, Vent, Vain, Rain, Rant, Lane, Saint, Taint, Stain, Slant, Event, Stern, Train, Satan, Enter, Siren, Naive, Tense, Raven, Learn, Never, Strain, Relent, Senate, Attain, Tavern, Natives, Alternatives

14. Art, Rat, Tar, Get, Cat, Tag, Eat, Gait, Grit, Tear, Rate, Gate, Cart, Tire, Tier, Cite, Rite, Irate, Trice, Grate, Crate, Great, Crater, Geriatric

15. Able, Bile, Goal, Toil, Boil, Glib, Lane, Nile, Late, Tale, Tile, Long, Tail, Nail, Bail, Bale, Gale, Lint, Line, Lion, Teal, Loan, Gloat, Bloat, Table, Noble, Glint, Bleat, Legion, Legation, Negotiable

16. Age, Get, Nag, Gem, Tag, Gate, Gnat, Gene, Game, Gent, Mega, Manage, Magnet, Management

17. Day, Tad, Cad, Aid, Din, Rod, Cod, Dot, Nod, Dart, Drat, Raid, Tidy, Toad, Road, Dirt, Yard, Card, Cord, Dirty, Tardy, Diary, Adroit, Dacoit, Diction, Dictionary

18. Host, Heir, Hire, Hurt, This, Hose, Shut, Shot, Thug, Gush, Rush, Thus, Those, House, Shore, Shirt, Girth, Shout, Short, Shire, Horse, Hoist, Ghost, Righteous

19. Fore, Foil, Loft, Rife, Four, Furl, Frill, Turf, Life, Lift, Rift, Fill, Fuel, Flit, Fire, Fort, File, Full, Foul, Flout, Flute, Flour, Furor, Flirt, Rifle, Cliff, Fruit, Flier, Forte, Force, Trifle, Filler, Filter, Fillet, Floriculture

20. Lot, Toe, Hoe, Too, Boo, Hot, Hole, Blot, Hoot, Toot, Tool, Loot, Bolt, Boot, Hotel, Booth, Tooth, Bottle, Bluetooth

21. Fast, Farm, Soft, Rift, Font, Sift, Raft, Fist, Fort, Fair, Firm, Foam, Foot, Form, Foist, Front, Frost, Faint, Mafia, Format, Transform, Formation, Transformation

22. Gate, Gait, Gang, Gear, Giant, Snag, Stag, Gist, Goat, Grin, Grit, Gong, Sage, Rage, Ogre, Sing, Ring, Great, Genes, Grant, Groin, Groan, Tiger, Grain, Grate, Grist, Stage, Greet, Tango, Range, Sting, Orange, Resign, String, Green, Singer, Ginger, Regent, Negate, Strong, Grange, Granite, Stagger, Sergeant, Segregation

23. All, Nab, Ban, Ball, Lab, Loan, Balloon

24. Our, Oar, Sour, Coir, Soar, Gracious

25. Part, Port, Sort, Trip, Rain, Trim, Grim, Trap, Ring, Pair, Grip, Rant, Prim, Harp, Pram, Grit, Mart, Mars, Horn, Roam, Gram, Rasp, Harm, Short, Marsh, Grist, Grant, Print, Shirt, Sharp, Strap, Strip, Train, Storm, Grasp, North, Girth, Mirth, Grain, Sport, Sprint, Shrimp, Strain, String, Rating, Spartan, Parting, Phantasmagoria

26. Cue, Cut, Jut, Use, Sue, Cute, Just, Jute, Suit, Suite, Juice, Justice

SPACE PERCEPTION

1. E	2. D	3. B	4. E	5. C	6. D	7. B
8. C	9. C	10. D	11. E	12. D	13. E	14. A
15. C	16. B	17. C	18. A	19. C	20. A	

In the answer figures shown below, a particular part of the figure has been indicated as the base and top to facilitate the explanation. However, remember, that it is a three dimensional figure which can be rotated in any angle so as to arrive at the correct answer. Use the suggestion as a starting point and do not think of it as an absolute rule.

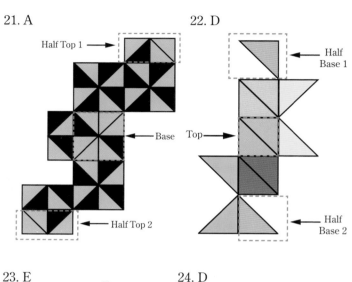

21. A
Half Top 1 →
← Base
← Half Top 2

22. D
← Half Base 1
Top →
← Half Base 2

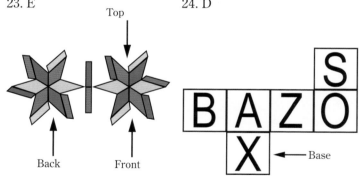

23. E
Top
Back   Front

24. D
	S	
B A Z O		
X ← Base		

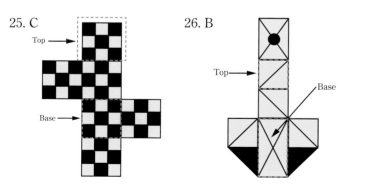

25. C
Top →
Base →

26. B
Top →
Base

228

CLUSTER

1. A   2. C   3. D   4. B   5. B   6. B   7. D

8. B   9. C   10. B   11. D   12. C   13. B   14. C

15. A   16. A   17. C   18. B   19. D   20. C

21. A   22. B

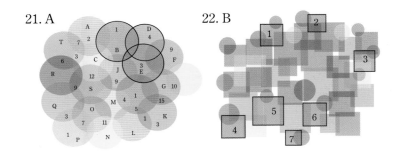

23. D   24. C

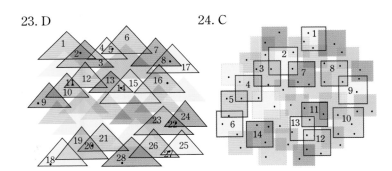

25. C   26. D

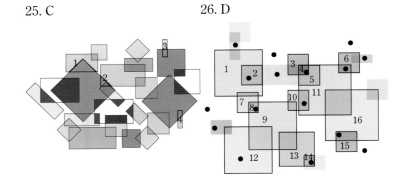

WORD FIND

1.

a	P	O	K	I	N	G
b	A	L	L	U	R	E
c	C	O	A	S	T	S
d	U	N	D	Y	E	D
e	L	E	T	T	E	R
f	B	R	A	Z	E	R

2.

Y	G	O	L	O	N	H	C	E	T	O	I	B	P
P	R	U	G	B	Y	B	S	I	D	T	R	O	H
A	C	S	H	O	R	T	P	U	T	T	O	G	G
R	H	O	R	T	E	C	U	H	T	U	R	N	Y
E	A	C	C	O	H	N	T	A	N	C	I	L	M
H	N	E	U	G	C	A	D	N	D	K	R	I	N
T	E	B	S	N	R	S	U	D	I	A	T	A	A
O	N	Y	T	I	A	K	G	B	E	I	A	I	S
I	A	E	I	S	R	I	N	A	L	M	I	M	T
D	M	E	D	I	C	I	N	L	D	R	H	R	I
R	R	O	D	T	A	N	R	L	A	A	C	A	C
Y	Y	R	U	T	A	G	E	L	D	A	R	T	S
A	A	U	N	E	S	A	M	O	E	N	S	N	Y
N	N	U	E	V	G	L	A	G	D	A	P	A	R
E	O	B	A	D	T	A	R	Y	I	C	A	C	A
M	S	I	L	A	N	C	A	N	O	E	I	N	G

3. Newton, Galileo, Darwin

4. DCGEAHJFBI
   Make hay while the sun shines.

5. ADECFHIGB
   A stitch in time saves nine.

6. IEAGDBHJFC
   A bad carpenter quarrels with his tools.

7.

a	D	E	L	I	R	I	A
b	A	R	M	B	A	N	D
c	B	I	O	G	E	N	Y
d	F	I	B	U	L	A	E
e	P	L	E	D	G	E	D
f	W	R	O	U	G	H	T
g	C	R	I	C	K	E	T

8.

a	S	P	A	N	G	L	E	D
b	A	E	R	O	B	I	C	S
c	C	O	M	P	U	T	E	D
d	H	U	M	A	N	I	S	T
e	A	G	R	O	N	O	M	Y
f	E	X	E	C	U	T	O	R
g	P	O	R	T	R	A	I	T
h	A	G	N	O	S	T	I	C

229

9.

a	A	S	P	E	R	S	E
b	A	D	M	I	R	A	L
c	M	A	J	E	S	T	Y
d	I	N	S	U	L	I	N
e	A	R	M	O	R	E	D
f	S	C	A	L	L	O	P
g	P	L	O	T	T	E	R

10.

```
Y G O L O N H C E T O I B P
P U E S A O B S I D T R O H Y
A C H G E R O N T O L O G Y S I
R E H O R T I C U L T U R E L I O
E A C C O U N T A N C Y L I
H N E U G A A D R D I R I O T H
T E B S N M E U C N A I T A T H E
O N Y T I E R G H E I A I T H E R
I A E I S R A I A L M I M R A P
D M E D I C I N E D R A H R A T Y
R R O D T C T R O A A C Y R A
Y Y R U R A T E L E T Y A T P A R
A A U S E S A M O E N S N Y A N
N N E E V G L A G D A P A R
E E B A D T A R Y I C A C A
M S I L A N R U O J O U R N
```

11.

```
D E L T A A I R L I N E S E S
A I R C A D H N A L F D D S S
A D P J I J G F B V N V N V M
B R T O D N H E J M O E S S N
E R A T I S H H J K L L L H V
L U I A M E R I A S S I W S C
A L I T E L A I F R A N O E I
S W I S I T I N O J K O M T F
N O T W E S T R I A L I T A I
A I I N D I H P A I I N I R C
H I O T H J O A I R I N D I A
T E U R A S O P I F H F U M P
F C S T S O H G L R G K H E Y
U F T H A S A L U A W I K A
L U F T I H D S K N B A V H H
L J G I H F G Y K C L J Y T A
B H B R U T F H K E H J M S C
S A I R C A N A D A A L L O N
```

12.

```
M A C R A A D G G G D H D F B
S I L I C D B L H B O E J K M
U N C A P G E M I N I W M L U
N M R K N L C B B M L N H J
M O O N O S O G M W O G H T M
I B M L H S G O O G H T M L P
C E L C A R O R C L T O L P
R P O L P T B F N B J P J L C
O B F J W S S U T B N A K K E
S V N M H I U F E H M C N J J
Y N N M M J V H L O H K B G N
S S T Q G J L U H J K A U N E
T M I V R O S O G R J R H N R
E H K H R D E W A V A D M P T
M N L E W A S R T R F C A O N
S B M W O U N S N S E N Z O C
Z E N N L E O P O L U V H J A
G I G E Z B B I N E E L P P A
```

13.

```
M R C E D A D F H J O L J F V
M E K H J D U H D D H F I F O
D D R Q V U J F S A S A V Y L
G G X C O R O L A F T C E X K
O C T A E V I A V I F C D X S
B M C S S D A W R C H T D S W
S H I C H J E S F C H D F S A
L V I K U Z U S U S U K C B G
L U F F U D T F V I G D T E N
A C Y O H J O F S K O D A W
H B E N Y O W A G O N C T C C
X G H S W X B Y S D F F O C C
U P F E D C J D D J E U Y Z V
A Q A A C Y C X T W D S O D I L
V D K D S V T D C Y S D T I L
```

14.

```
C D M T B Z B Z U W L A F D J
J I U R W R G Y L A K F O B C
Y K U L I W T Z W C R L A H L
H H M F E L X S V C F B D L N
L M G A L F N D K I P C G R X
Z J I Q M O X W W M E Y H O K
T V O J L T J C I O U B U V S
N H U D Z Q O V W S N R I R E
F A C H Y F W U K D Q Q T L I
Q U F M H W I F Z V A O V M I
H W X L E B A O O A N X E D N
X P Z G F S E C N R U Q K W C
M A I N R N B I A E N I E S X
N G F A D B I L T Q I F E I S
```

15.

A	N	G	E	L	I	N	A	J	O	L	I	E	L	Q
A	F	J	G	T	H	K	C	S	C	Y	B	D	T	V
N	I	J	I	K	L	L	V	D	V	C	B	F	F	V
J	Z	C	C	J	C	S	H	D	J	D	D	D	G	G
E	T	G	O	U	F	S	F	N	F	C	C	M	R	C
N	A	J	U	L	C	D	F	F	I	L	J	Y	E	D
N	Y	H	K	I	E	F	E	T	R	W	F	H	T	O
I	L	I	A	K	K	I	D	W	C	F	F	A	K	
F	O	R	O	R	V	B	I	F	J	L	L	T	G	R
E	L	D	D	H	B	M	H	E	W	M	W	V	K	R
R	O	A	N	G	E	R	A	G	R	E	A	T	F	J
L	A	O	M	A	R	I	L	Y	N	M	O	N	R	O	E
O	T	R	W	T	I	O	V	A	Q	Q	F	V	H	I
P	Z	P	O	G	S	D	R	V	H	H	T	G	R	T

16.

L	I	S	B	D	F	G	H	D	E	N	B	A
A	R	G	A	T	N	A	N	A	F	C	J	F
G	P	O	R	G	L	A	G	K	L	V	D	C
U	T	K	G	A	R	D	X	B	X	R	I	G
T	R	A	N	V	A	A	Y	I	T	L	E	
R	O	F	E	C	G	L	N	K	G	B	V	R
O	P	L	P	E	B	C	S	T	A	R	K	M
P	R	C	N	R	F	C	R	A	I	G	Z	A
D	P	O	R	U	H	D	T	L	A	N	I	N
S	D	H	J	F	L	L	H	Y	S	P	A	I	N
A	S	P	A	N	I	A	L	D	A	N	L	E	C
A	E	R	Z	I	Y	L	F	F	F	T	E	N
R	A	A	I	Y	T	D	D	G	I	X	F	V
B	R	S	T	R	U	J	L	D	V	N	H	D
B	F	H	Y	I	H	F	E	F	O	F	D	

17.

A	N	N	A	K	O	U	R	N	I	K	O	V	A	A
U	N	S	E	D	B	S	D	D	B	S	D	B	R	
R	E	G	N	T	Y	N	N	T	Y	N	T	Z	Z	
O	R	U	R	E	R	N	E	E	R	E	E	H		
N	L	N	O	L	E	E	E	L	E	E	L	S		
A	E	E	G	D	D	D	A	T	D	A	B			
L	A	D	R	Z	L	L	A	E	D	T	J			
D	D	R	E	R	G	A	M	O	G	E	O	W		
I	E	E	F	B	I	T	P	A	T	D	A	U		
N	E	S	E	D	M	R	D	D	S	D	B	P		
H	R	D	D	N	A	Y	G	N	A	I	N	T	K	
O	P	U	E	S	I	R	N	N	E	R	E	E	T	
R	A	N	R	E	O	E	L	E	E	L	H			
N	E	E	D	A	R	D	D	A	D	D	A	Y		
E	S	D	R	L	S	E	L	L	T	E	L	T	E	
S	A	R	P	M	A	S	E	T	E	P	E	O	G	

18.

A	T	E	L	B	W	O	C	S	O	M	M
U	E	S	E	D	I	S	O	D	F	I	N
C	H	I	N	A	T	Y	N	N	R	I	N
E	R	R	B	P	K	R	A	S	A	D	
R	L	M	N	O	L	N	E	E	N	I	
N	U	O	T	N	O	R	O	T	K	A	
M	U	M	B	E	T	E	R	T	F	O	
S	Y	R	P	A	R	I	S	O	U	B	
S	L	E	L	I	O	I	N	R	M	O	
H	A	P	A	N	M	S	C	D	T	O	
A	T	D	G	D	E	Y	E	A	T	L	
N	I	U	N	I	T	D	N	E	W	O	
G	L	O	N	D	O	N	E	L	C		
H	E	E	N	G	L	E	N	D	A	D	
A	B	D	Y	L	T	Y	L	L	T	E	
U	D	N	A	K	R	O	Y	W	E	N	

19.

a	J	U	S	T	I	F	Y
b	L	A	T	E	R	A	L
c	E	N	C	L	A	S	P
d	P	I	C	K	A	X	E
e	T	R	O	U	P	E	R
f	A	E	R	O	S	O	L
g	R	I	N	G	L	E	T

20.

a	D	A	B	B	E	D
b	B	E	D	L	A	M
c	B	I	F	O	L	D
d	A	F	F	I	R	M
e	B	A	R	O	N	Y
f	C	R	I	N	G	E

21.

a	F	E	S	T	E	R
b	G	L	O	W	E	R
c	B	A	U	B	L	E
d	P	U	M	M	E	L
e	C	L	A	R	E	T
f	T	R	A	I	T	S

22.

a	P	R	E	L	I	M
b	P	E	P	P	E	R
c	O	W	L	E	T	S
d	P	O	E	T	R	Y
e	L	A	U	R	E	L
f	N	E	C	T	A	R

23.

Y	G	H	L	O	N	H	C	E	T	Y	Y
L	L	E	A	T	H	E	N	S	S	T	
O	O	L	H	O	R	T	P	U	T	I	
N	N	S	R	T	E	C	U	H	O	C	
E	D	I	A	O	H	N	T	A	C	O	
H	O	N	U	N	C	A	D	N	K	I	
T	N	K	S	N	G	S	U	D	H	X	
O	I	T	I	A	E	G	B	O			
I	A	E	I	S	R	I	L	A	X		
M	E	L	B	O	U	R	N	E	M	M	
R	R	O	D	T	P	A	R	I	S	A	
B	A	R	C	E	L	O	N	A	A		
A	A	U	N	E	S	A	M	O	E	N	

B	P	H	F	X	V	E	S	A	Z	U	N	K	F	S
D	E	R	R	T	M	S	B	I	V	B	X	C	G	I
H	M	M	A	P	I	O	C	S	C	D	D	C	B	E
L	F	A	Q	W	S	Y	K	H	I	N	Y	C	W	M
N	E	R	I	C	S	Y	I	K	H	D	U	L	X	E
A	U	C	A	L	R	E	O	F	E	L	A	X	X	N
S	T	E	G	N	Y	R	A	S	S	N	D	U	L	S
O	C	E	N	O	K	I	S	O	M	W	T	R	N	I
N	C	C	U	K	G	E	C	M	O	X	K	T	S	R
S	U	S	S	E	X	S	S	E	L	P	Q	Y	E	K
C	O	U	R	S	G	S	A	R	S	E	R	N	D	L
E	N	F	S	A	C	O	U	S	U	R	R	E	Y	O
W	I	L	T	S	H	I	R	E	E	Q	R	R	D	V
Y	S	T	W	C	K	K	Q	T	R	H	U	R	L	F
Y	X	O	D	J	V	Y	B	B	K	R	O	T	O	R
C	N	M	S	F	V	J	N	D	G	G	B	Y	R	N

REPOSITION

1.

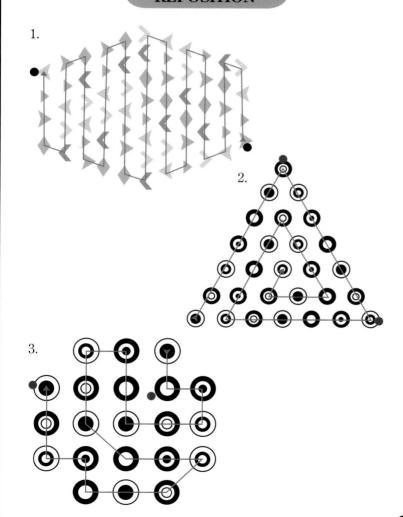

2.

3.

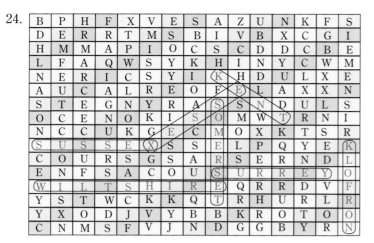

4.

5.

6.

7.

8.

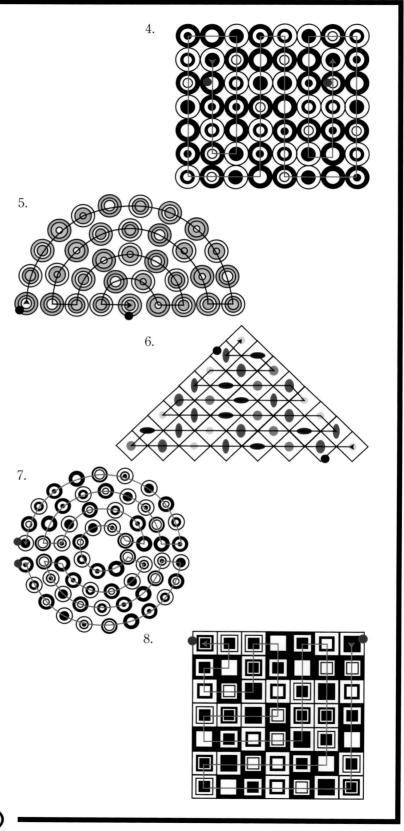

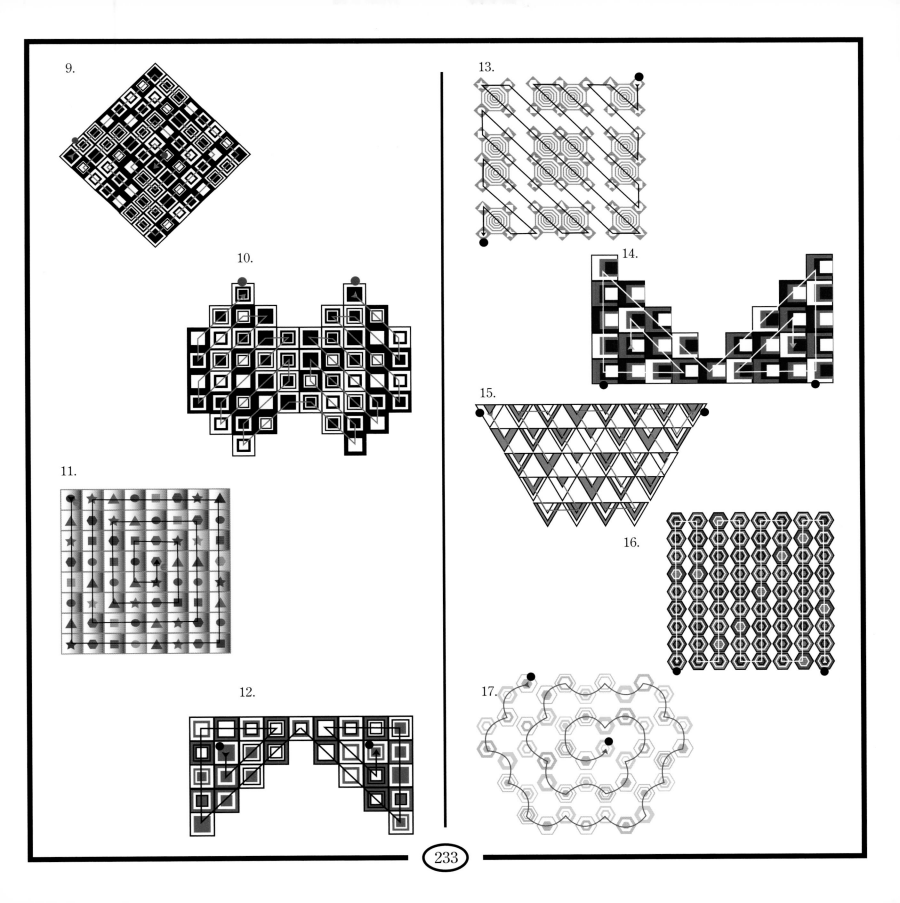

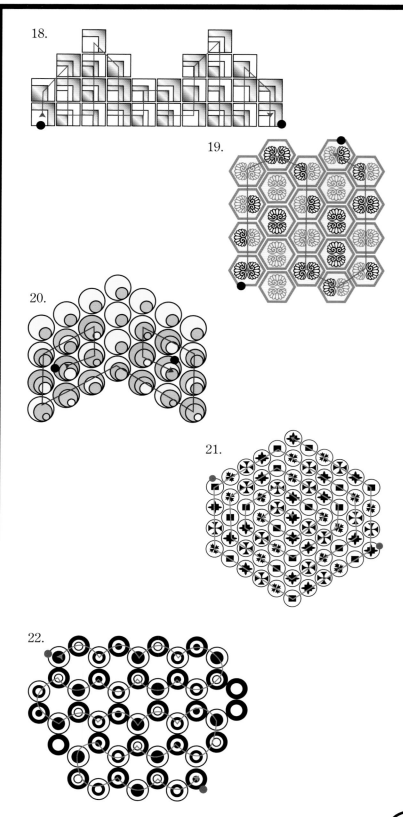

18.

19.

20.

21.

22.

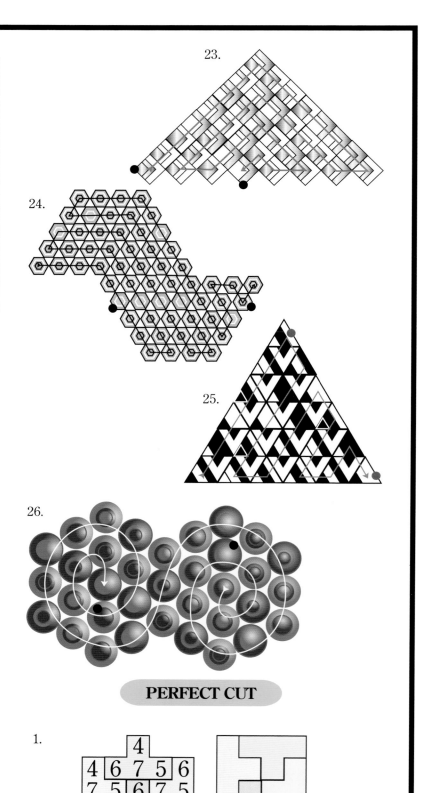

23.

24.

25.

26.

PERFECT CUT

1.

		4		
4	6	7	5	6
7	5	6	7	5
6	4	7	5	4

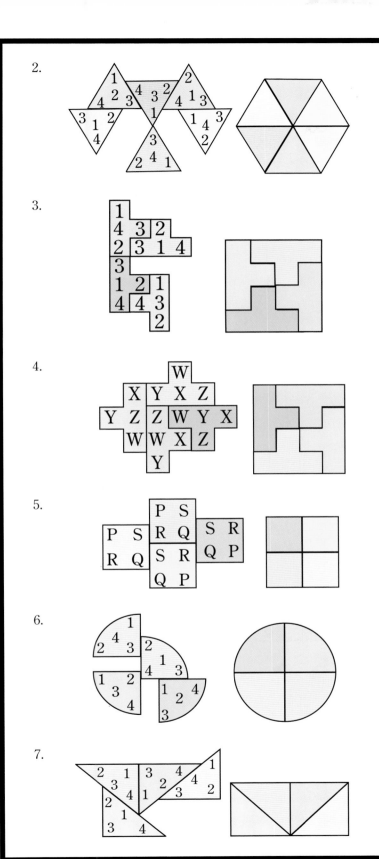

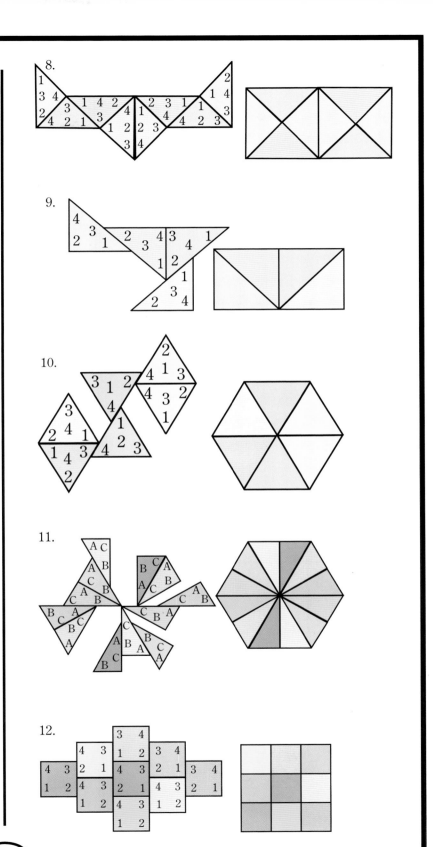

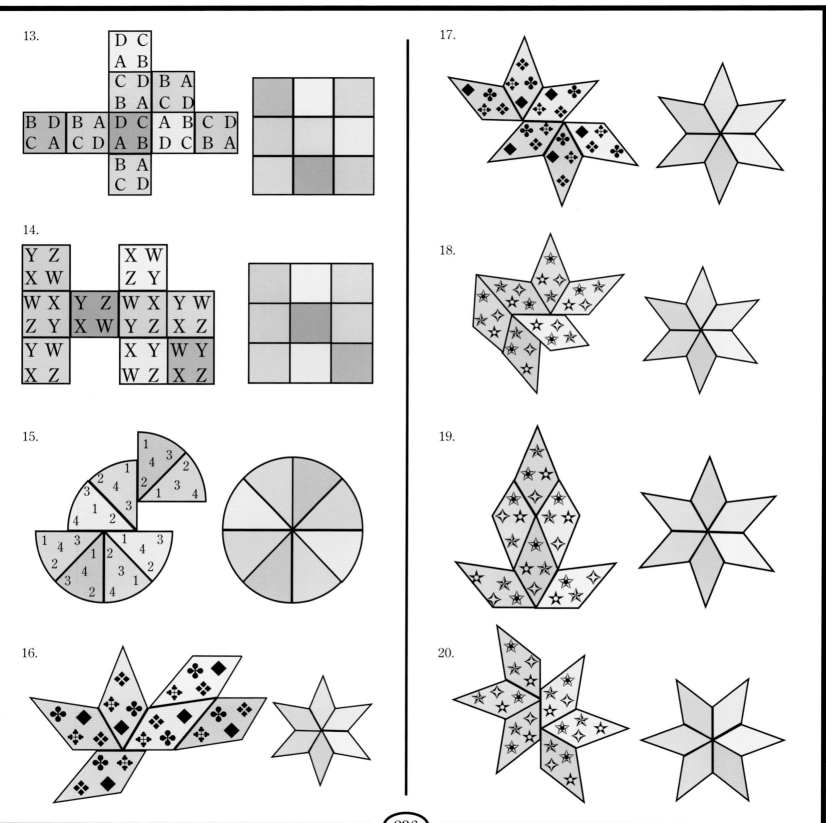

13.

14.

15.

16.

17.

18.

19.

20.

236

21.

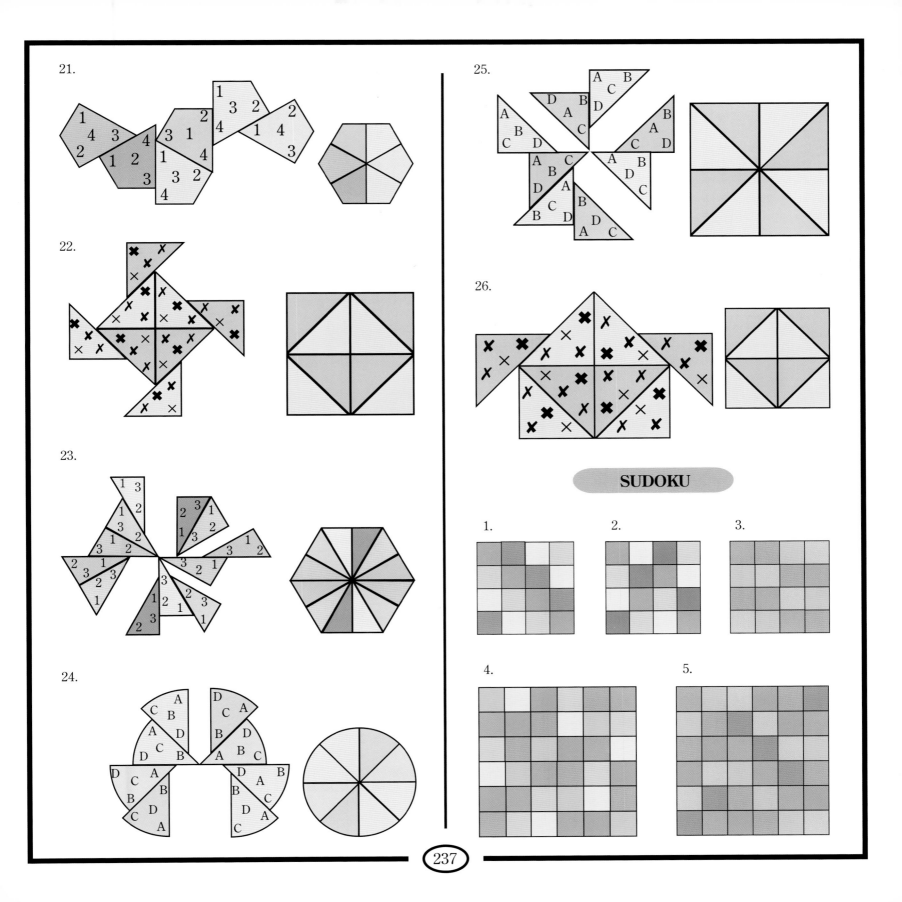

22.

23.

24.

25.

26.

SUDOKU

1.

2.

3.

4.

5.

6.

7.

8.

9.

10.

11.

Ω	+	□	√	☆	×	◇	Δ	O
Δ	☆	◇	□	Ω	O	+	×	√
√	O	×	Δ	+	◇	Ω	□	☆
□	Δ	+	◇	√	Ω	O	☆	×
×	√	Ω	☆	O	+	Δ	◇	□
O	◇	☆	×	Δ	□	√	Ω	+
+	×	Δ	Ω	□	√	☆	O	◇
☆	□	O	+	◇	Δ	×	√	Ω
◇	Ω	√	O	×	☆	□	+	Δ

12.

Δ	O	×	□	◇	+	☆	Ω	√
☆	√	+	Δ	×	Ω	◇	□	O
◇	□	Ω	☆	O	√	+	×	Δ
O	+	☆	√	Δ	×	□	◇	Ω
Ω	◇	□	O	+	☆	Δ	√	×
×	Δ	√	◇	Ω	□	O	☆	+
+	×	Δ	Ω	☆	◇	√	O	□
√	Ω	◇	+	□	O	×	Δ	☆
□	☆	O	×	√	Δ	Ω	+	◇

13.

+	Δ	Ω	□	×	☆	√	◇	O
O	×	◇	√	+	Ω	Δ	☆	□
□	☆	√	Δ	O	◇	×	+	Ω
Δ	Ω	+	◇	☆	×	O	□	√
◇	√	☆	Ω	□	O	+	×	Δ
×	□	O	+	Δ	√	◇	Ω	☆
√	◇	□	O	Ω	+	☆	Δ	×
☆	O	Δ	×	◇	□	Ω	√	+
Ω	+	×	☆	√	Δ	□	O	◇

14.

☆	+	Δ	O	×	◇	Ω	□	√
□	×	√	☆	Ω	+	◇	Δ	O
Ω	O	◇	√	Δ	□	☆	×	+
×	Δ	Ω	□	O	☆	√	+	◇
O	√	□	+	◇	×	Δ	☆	Ω
+	◇	☆	Δ	√	Ω	×	O	□
Δ	Ω	×	◇	□	O	+	√	☆
◇	□	+	×	☆	√	O	Ω	Δ
√	☆	O	Ω	+	Δ	□	◇	×

15.

☆	◇	+	Ω	×	√	Δ	O	□
Ω	O	□	☆	Δ	+	√	×	◇
×	√	Δ	□	◇	O	Ω	☆	+
+	×	◇	O	√	Ω	☆	□	Δ
□	Δ	O	◇	☆	×	+	√	Ω
√	☆	Ω	Δ	+	□	×	◇	O
Δ	Ω	√	×	□	◇	O	+	☆
O	□	×	+	Ω	☆	◇	Δ	√
◇	+	☆	√	O	Δ	□	Ω	×

16.

☆	◇	Ω	×	√	+	□	O	△
O	×	△	□	Ω	◇	+	√	☆
+	√	□	O	☆	△	◇	Ω	×
√	Ω	◇	△	□	☆	O	×	+
□	☆	O	+	×	Ω	√	△	◇
×	△	+	√	◇	O	☆	□	Ω
◇	O	×	☆	△	□	Ω	+	√
Ω	+	√	◇	O	×	△	☆	□
△	□	☆	Ω	+	√	×	◇	O

17.

+	☆	△	□	×	√	Ω	O	◇
√	◇	×	☆	O	Ω	△	□	+
Ω	□	O	◇	+	△	×	√	☆
□	O	√	Ω	◇	×	+	☆	△
◇	△	Ω	+	√	☆	□	×	O
☆	×	+	△	□	O	◇	Ω	√
×	Ω	◇	O	☆	+	√	△	□
△	+	☆	√	Ω	□	O	◇	×
O	√	□	×	△	◇	☆	+	Ω

18.

×	√	☆	◇	+	Ω	\	O	□
\	◇	□	×	√	O	Ω	☆	+
Ω	+	O	□	\	☆	×	◇	√
□	△	Ω	☆	◇	×	+	√	O
O	×	+	Ω	□	√	◇	\	☆
◇	☆	√	△	O	+	□	×	Ω
√	O	△	+	Ω	◇	☆	□	×
+	□	×	√	☆	△	O	Ω	◇
☆	Ω	◇	O	×	□	√	+	△

19.

Ω	+	×	O	□	√	☆	◇	△
□	☆	◇	Ω	△	+	√	×	O
√	△	O	◇	×	☆	Ω	□	+
+	√	☆	□	Ω	◇	△	O	×
×	◇	Ω	△	+	O	□	√	☆
△	O	□	☆	√	×	+	Ω	◇
☆	□	△	×	O	Ω	◇	+	√
O	Ω	√	+	◇	△	×	☆	□
◇	×	+	√	☆	□	O	△	Ω

20.

+	□	O	√	△	Ω	×	☆	◇
√	△	☆	+	◇	×	O	□	Ω
◇	×	Ω	□	☆	O	+	△	√
O	◇	□	Ω	+	√	☆	×	△
☆	Ω	√	×	□	△	◇	O	+
×	+	△	◇	O	☆	Ω	√	□
Ω	O	+	☆	√	□	△	◇	×
□	☆	×	△	Ω	◇	√	+	O
△	√	◇	O	×	+	□	Ω	☆

21.

□	√	+	O	Ω	×	△	◇	☆
O	△	☆	□	+	◇	×	Ω	√
Ω	◇	×	△	√	☆	□	+	O
√	☆	Ω	×	□	+	◇	O	△
+	O	□	◇	☆	△	Ω	√	×
△	×	◇	√	O	Ω	☆	□	+
×	Ω	O	☆	◇	√	+	△	□
☆	+	√	Ω	△	□	O	×	◇
◇	□	△	+	×	O	√	☆	Ω

22.

△	◇	√	+	×	□	O	☆	Ω
×	+	□	☆	O	Ω	√	◇	△
Ω	☆	O	◇	△	√	□	+	×
+	√	Ω	△	☆	O	◇	×	□
O	□	△	×	√	◇	☆	Ω	+
☆	×	◇	Ω	□	+	△	O	√
√	Ω	+	□	◇	☆	×	△	O
□	△	☆	O	Ω	×	+	√	◇
◇	O	×	√	+	△	Ω	□	☆

23.

O	√	△	□	×	☆	◇	+	Ω
◇	×	Ω	+	△	√	O	☆	□
+	☆	□	O	◇	Ω	×	△	√
Ω	□	☆	×	+	◇	√	O	△
×	+	O	△	√	□	Ω	◇	☆
√	△	◇	☆	Ω	O	□	×	+
☆	◇	√	Ω	O	△	+	□	×
□	Ω	+	◇	☆	×	△	√	O
△	O	×	√	□	+	☆	Ω	◇

24.

×	△	√	Ω	☆	O	□	◇	+
Ω	+	◇	□	△	×	O	√	☆
O	☆	□	◇	√	+	×	△	Ω
☆	□	O	√	+	△	Ω	×	◇
△	√	+	×	◇	Ω	☆	O	□
◇	Ω	×	☆	O	□	△	+	√
√	◇	Ω	O	×	☆	+	□	△
□	×	△	+	Ω	√	◇	☆	O
+	O	☆	△	□	◇	√	Ω	×